KELLY, Regina

Paul Revere

PAUL REVERE

Colonial Craftsman

Paul Revere:

ILLUSTRATED BY HARVEY KIDDER

Colonial Craftsman

REGINA Z. KELLY

HOUGHTON MIFFLIN COMPANY · BOSTON

NEW YORK · ATLANTA · GENEVA, ILL. · DALLAS · PALO ALTO

Contents

CHAPTER 1

Clark's Wharf

 Let's see you dive. Go on. I dare you."

Paul Revere looked down into the dark waters of Boston Bay. Pieces of garbage, dead fish, barrel staves, and scraps of wood floated on the surface. Sea gulls bobbed up and down on the waves, shrieking and swooping as they searched for food. Broken wooden stumps stuck out here and there.

"You're scared because it's high. You know you are."

The skin on Paul's bare arms and chest prickled. As long as he could remember, he had swum near Clark's Wharf. But always before, he had waded in. Now he was on the wharf, and it was ten feet high, he guessed.

He remembered what his mother said each

7

time he came home wet and dirty from swimming at the water front. "Your Cousin Davy was drowned falling off the wharf!" she would scream at him.

Back of Paul, along the whole length of the wharf, were shops, warehouses, and counting rooms. Dozens of shoppers went in and out of doorways on this busy Saturday afternoon. But no one paid any attention to Paul and the two boys with him. It was a warm day in August, and boys diving along the wharf were a common sight in Boston.

"I'll bet you a penny you're afraid to dive."

Paul turned and looked angrily at John Dyer, who had been daring him. He was fifteen, five years older than Paul. But John played sometimes with the younger boys, perhaps because he was short and thin and boys of his own age bullied him.

"I'll show you if I'm afraid," said Paul, beginning to pull off his breeches. His full-sleeved linen shirt was already in a heap on the wharf.

"Don't do it, Paul. You'll hit your head on one of those stumps," warned Josiah Flagg. He was a year younger than Paul and followed him everywhere.

But Paul's dark eyes were on the water. With a quick stretch of his arms, he leaped and was over the side of the wharf. A half minute later, he bobbed up and kicked his heels while he held onto a stump and grinned up at the boys.

Josiah was waving and jumping up and down. "I told you he wasn't scared. Paul's never scared!" he shrieked at John. "Now get your penny out."

Paul waved to the boys and swam lazily toward a big sailing vessel that was anchored a hundred feet away. He'd collect his penny later.

He floated near the huge ship. Sailors were washing the deck and polishing the brass rails. Along the wharf were fishing boats and merchant ships. Clark's Wharf was next in length to Long Wharf, which stretched two thousand feet into Boston Bay.

Long Wharf was the longest wharf in the city.

"Get out of the way, boy."

Paul looked up. The ship's cook was leaning over the rail with a big pail of garbage. Paul swam a few strokes, then grabbed the rudder. He'd rest for a while.

The town of Boston was to Paul's left, its buildings crowded to the water's edge. Church spires pierced the clear blue of the

sky, and the sound of bells floated over the bay. Three hills stretched across the back of the town. The highest was Beacon Hill, in the middle. Crowning it was a tall pole topped by a tar barrel filled with turpentine. If danger threatened Boston, the barrel would be set on fire and become a beacon for the town.

The crowd had thinned now on Clark's

Wharf. Walking slowly toward Josiah and John was a stout man with a full red face and a double chin resting in a nest of lace ruffles. He wore a red silk coat and white satin breeches.

Paul recognized the man. He was Thomas Hancock, the richest merchant in Boston. Once in a while, he ordered pieces of silver from Paul's father. They would be only small pieces as a rule, for Thomas Hancock ordered everything important from London.

Holding onto Mr. Hancock's hand was a small boy about seven. "That must be John Hancock, Mr. Hancock's nephew," thought Paul. Except for the fact that the colors the boy wore were blue and white, he was dressed exactly like his uncle in a long waistcoat, a full-skirted coat, knee breeches, and buckled shoes. He even had on a well-brushed wig under his three-cornered hat. He almost ran to keep up with his uncle's slow step.

When Mr. Hancock came near Josiah and John Dyer, he paused to look at the sign in front of the shop where Doctor Clark sold drugs. Then Mr. Hancock went indoors, first motioning to his nephew to remain outside.

Just then, Josiah waved to Paul and pointed to the setting sun. "Come get your penny!" he shouted. "John's going home."

Paul began to swim. It must be near supper time. If he didn't get the wood in for the kitchen fire, his mother would give him a beating.

A few minutes later, Paul pulled himself over the edge of the wharf. "I'll take my penny now," he said as he wiped his wet body and dark hair with his shirt and pulled on his breeches.

"I told John you could dive from the wharf," Josiah repeated in triumph. "I wish *I* had bet him a penny."

"Did you dive from the top of this wharf?" asked an awed and childish voice.

The boys had not noticed that John Hancock had moved near them. His eyes were round with wonder as he stared at Paul.

"How would you like to do it?" asked John Dyer roughly.

13

"I can't swim," said John Hancock, backing hastily away.

"Of course you can. Give it a try," said John Dyer, following the boy and grabbing him by the arm.

"I can't, sir. I really can't." Frightened tears were in John Hancock's eyes, as he tried to pull away.

John Dyer's hold on the small boy's arm tightened as he began pulling him toward the edge of the wharf.

"Oh, let me go, sir. Please let me go. I can't swim." The boy dragged his feet and held back as hard as he could, but he was no match for John Dyer. John had pulled him now to within a few inches from the edge of the wharf.

"Let the boy go!" Paul called sharply. He knew John Dyer had no intention of pushing the little boy into the bay. Dyer was probably angry because he had lost his bet and his penny, and was easing his own bad temper. But John Hancock was white with fright and too shaken now even to resist.

14

"Let him go, I said," repeated Paul angrily when John Dyer pushed the boy a little closer to the edge.

"You make me," answered John Dyer.

Paul ran forward and seized John Hancock's other arm. There was a tug between the two older boys. Josiah jumped up and down with excitement. In the struggle, the penny slipped from John Dyer's hand and rolled away. Josiah rushed to stop it, but shook his head sadly as it dropped into the water.

"You'll give me another penny!" shouted Paul, still trying to get possession of John Hancock.

Suddenly the coat sleeve that John Dyer was pulling on tore away, and the small boy tumbled against Paul. At the same moment, Mr. Hancock came out of Doctor Clark's shop.

"Let's run!" shrieked Josiah. "Mr. Hancock's coming."

Instantly, John Dyer dropped his hold on the boy and with one leap followed Josiah

15

into an alleyway between two buildings. The sudden release made John Hancock fall to the ground.

"What's this? What's this?" bellowed an angry voice. "How did you tear your coat, lad? And where did you get that mud? Have you been fighting?"

Paul turned around. He had been helping the small boy get to his feet and brush his clothes.

Mr. Hancock was hurrying toward them. Behind him was Robin, Doctor Clark's Negro page boy, in his red and yellow suit and shiny black wig. He held a silver tray piled neatly with small white packages from the drug shop.

John Hancock was on his feet now, but trembling with fright. "I wasn't fighting, sir. Truly, I wasn't," he cried, his thin voice lost in his uncle's roar.

"The nice new waistcoat that your Aunt Lydia embroidered in gold thread, all covered with mud!" shouted Mr. Hancock, paying no attention to his nephew's denial.

17

"She'll need the headache powders I have bought for her, when she learns that her nephew has been fighting like a common North End boy."

Paul's back bristled. He was a North End boy and no more common than Mr. Hancock, even if he was the richest man in Boston. He and Paul's father had both worked on Anne Street, not far from where Paul now lived, when they were boys. But Thomas Hancock had married his rich employer's daughter and thus started to make the biggest fortune in New England.

"He wasn't fighting, sir," said Paul. "I tore his coat."

"You tore his coat!" roared Mr. Hancock. "You'll pay for this, lad. I'll have the law on you."

But young John was pulling at the skirt of his uncle's coat. "It isn't true, sir!" he shrieked. "This boy kept the other one from throwing me into the water. My coat was torn when this boy tried to pull me away. He was helping me."

"What's this? What's this? Did someone try to drown you? What happened, lad?" Mr. Hancock's face was suddenly filled with alarm. He leaned down and put his arm around his nephew as if to keep him from harm.

Quickly, between half sobs, the small boy told the story.

"And you would have been drowned if this boy had not saved you. And your Aunt Lydia and I would have had no heir." The red in Mr. Hancock's face had paled a little, and he held his nephew more closely.

"It wasn't as bad as that, sir," said Paul, feeling uncomfortable. "John Dyer didn't really mean to push your nephew into the water."

But Mr. Hancock paid no attention to Paul. He only continued to brush his nephew's coat and to give him loving pats.

"This boy lost the penny that he had won for diving from the wharf," said John Hancock, looking with sympathy at Paul.

"Lost his penny, you say? Well, we'll

make up for that," said Mr. Hancock, now looking at Paul. From his pocket he took his purse. "Here's a gold sovereign for you, lad," he said. "It's worth two hundred and forty pennies, but not as much as my nephew's life."

Paul stared at the glittering coin in his hand. Then he tried to stutter his thanks.

Mr. Hancock gave him a sharp stare. "Aren't you the son of Paul Revere, the silversmith on Fish Street?"

Paul nodded.

"Well, tell your father I'll be in his shop on Monday to order a silver tea set for Mrs. Hancock."

With that, Mr. Hancock took his nephew's hand and strode away. Little John took skipping steps to keep up with his uncle's pace. Behind them stepped Robin the page, swishing his red and yellow coat and holding the silver tray high.

Paul bit into the gold coin, then tied it carefully into a corner of his shirt. Whistling happily, he raced toward home. He was late, and he could hardly wait until his father heard that Mr. Hancock was going to order a silver tea set. Not a spoon or a porringer, but a whole big tea set. But Paul must tell his story fast, before his mother took down the switch.

CHAPTER 2

Bell Ringer
for Christ Church

Paul ran to the North Writing School in Love Lane.* It was nearly eight o'clock, and Master Hicks was at the door ringing the bell for the morning session.

"Hurry up," Paul called to short-legged Josiah, who was panting after him. "We'll be late."

Paul held out his hand and yanked Josiah along. A half minute later, they ducked under the master's arm as he sounded the last note of the bell.

This was Paul's fourth year at the North

---

* Now Tileston Street. See map, pages 54, 55.

Writing School. He had gone there ever since he was eight. The sons of most of the tradesmen living in the North End of Boston were his classmates. Boys like Sam Adams and John Hancock went to the Boston Latin School, preparing to go to Harvard College.

Paul's school was a two-story wooden building. Reading was taught on one floor and writing on the other. The only tuition charged by the school was five shillings a year for the firewood.

Paul slid into his place in the back of the room and neatly arranged his writing material. He had two copybooks, some sheets of rough brown paper, a ruler, an inkhorn, two quill pens, and a pen knife to sharpen the ends of his pens. A plummet hung by a string attached to the desk. This was a piece of lead fashioned to a point which Paul used to make lines on his paper.

Gradually the noise of heavy shoes and voices ended, and the boys were in their places. "Good morning," Master Hicks greeted them, looking sharply around the room to see that every boy was in his place.

"Good morning," sang out the boys together.

The Lord's Prayer was said, and then they were ready for the day's work. The room was bare, for there were no pictures or maps on the walls. Already the air was heavy and stale. Very little light or air came through the grimy windows. Master Hicks sat at a desk on a platform in front of the room. An old globe and a few worn books were on the desk. On one side hung a thick switch in easy reach of the teacher's hand.

Big boys like Paul were in the rear of the room. They sat on a long bench facing a high desk. In front of the room were the small boys on long backless benches. The feet of the smallest ones did not even reach the floor.

"Take out your sum books," Master Hicks told the older boys when the morning prayer was ended.

The teacher had no textbook, but he was a good "arithmeticker" and had a "sum book" of his own from which he read rules and problems aloud to the boys. They copied the rules over and over until they knew them by heart. Sometimes, the rules were in rhyme and were easy to learn. The sums would be worked again and again, until somehow even the poorest student got the correct answer. While the older boys worked in their sum books, the younger ones recited the multiplication tables in a chorus to Master Hicks.

Paul began to work at the lesson. He liked to write with round, clear letters and to do arithmetic. He had the feeling that something had been done properly when he got the correct answer to a problem. He had made the sum book himself of rough brown paper on which he had ruled the lines with his plummet.

The pages of the book had been sewn together by Paul's mother between heavy cardboard covers. She had also made the ink in his inkhorn by boiling the roots of swamp maple that Paul had cut in the woods.

26

There were two fat geese in their small yard at home whose quills were saved each year for the pens that Paul and his father used. Master Hicks sharpened the pens belonging to the small boys, but Paul had his own pen knife.

Paul valued his sum book highly and expected to keep and use it all his life. On the first page, he had written,

Steal not this Book, for if You **Do**
The Devil will be after You.

Not even at the Latin School were students taught when and how to use capital letters.

"Multiplication," Paul wrote neatly as the heading for his page today. Then he used his plummet to divide the page into two parts and wrote "Examples" at the top of each column.

So far, Paul could multiply only eight figures by five. He envied little Johnny Tileston, who sat to the left of him. Johnny could multiply fifteen figures by fifteen more and work a sum that took all of a page. But Johnny was the smartest boy in the school and planned one day to be a writing master.

Josiah, who sat on Paul's right, was slow. When Master Hicks was not looking, Paul helped Josiah with his sums. He was still copying the lesson which Paul had finished two years ago.

Five and two together make .... $\dfrac{7}{1}$

Seven and one together make 8

wrote Josiah slowly.

His pen spluttered, and his fingers got stained with ink. Once in a while, he wiped his fingers on his breeches or in his hair. Soon there were smears of ink even on his cheeks.

The last of the sand trickled through the small hourglass on the teacher's desk. Paul yawned and stretched. There were shuffling noises all around him now. Small boys tried to reach the floor with their feet. Tall boys whose legs were too long for their bench stood up a bit.

Master Hicks gave a loud bang on his desk with his ruler. "We'll have our spelling lesson now," he said. From the desk, he picked up his copy of Dilworth's Speller, and pushed his steel-rimmed spectacles up on his nose. The boys in the rear of the room turned around, and the small ones in the front straightened on their benches. They all folded their hands.

"Spell molasses," shouted Master Hicks.

"M-o-l-a-s-s-e-s," sang out all the boys in a chorus.

All spelled it correctly except Josiah. "M-o-l-a-s-e-s," yelled Josiah.

"What's that? What's that?" cried Master Hicks, cocking his head to one side. "Someone has spelled the word wrong."

He glared at Josiah and fingered the switch by his desk.

"Two s's," whispered Paul. He looked straight ahead and scarcely moved his lips.

Up went the teacher's head. This time he stared at Paul, who looked back with a round, innocent gaze. The rest of the boys almost held their breaths. They seemed a little disappointed when the master did not reach for the switch.

"Now spell molasses again," said Master Hicks.

This time Josiah sang out the letters loudly and correctly.

For the next hour, the spelling lesson continued. Once in a while, a word was repeated. But Josiah watched Paul's lips closely and managed not to make another mistake.

At eleven o'clock, the pupils were dismissed for their noonday dinner. They would return at one o'clock and remain until five in the afternoon. John Dyer was waiting at the door when Paul rushed out with Josiah after him. John no longer attended school, but helped his father in his leather shop. He was still friendly, however, with the younger boys.

"I want you to come with me to Christ Church," said John, grabbing Paul by the arm. "I have a job for you. You, too, Josiah."

30

"I can't go to Christ Church," said Paul, pulling away. "My father would beat me."

"Why should he beat you for going to a church?" asked Josiah.

"Because Christ Church is a Church of England, and we are Puritans," said Paul. "My father says only idol worshipers go to a Church of England."

Paul wasn't quite sure what an "idol worshiper" was. He guessed his father meant that there were statues and things in a Church of England, before which people

31

knelt and prayed. Puritan churches were very plain and had no ornaments. Mr. Revere was as strict about his religion as the first Puritans who had come to Massachusetts.

"I don't want you to work in the church," said John, "just in the belfry. You'll earn two shillings a week."

Paul hesitated. "What's the job?" he asked.

"Ringing the bells."

"How often must we go?"

"Two hours a week to practice, and when the bells have to be rung for services or funerals, and such."

Paul frowned. "That's a lot of times."

"But there will be six of us to do the work," urged John.

"We could go look," said Josiah. "We went at Christmas time to see the greens. You remember how good they smelled?"

Paul nodded. Puritan churches were never decorated at Christmas. But Christ Church had been gay with holly wreaths and pine branches.

"Did your father beat you at Christmas time when you went to Christ Church?" asked John.

Paul shook his head. "He never knew I went. But last week when he found out I had gone to the West Street Church to listen to Reverend Mayhew preach, my father gave me a beating."

"But Reverend Mayhew is a Puritan preacher," said Josiah. "What's wrong with listening to him?"

"I don't know," said Paul. "My father says that Reverend Mayhew says things in his sermons that aren't the truth, and that the Puritans won't let him preach in our churches, if he keeps on saying those things."

"Well, maybe your father won't find out if you go to the belfry of Christ Church," said John. He turned to Josiah. "Will your father beat you if you go to Christ Church?"

"Not if I bring home two shillings a week," said Josiah.

"Let's go, then," said John. "The sexton is waiting for us."

33

The three boys ran to the next corner on Love Lane and turned right for a block to Christ Church, on Salem Street. It was the oldest church in Boston, and its steeple was the highest in the North End.

The sexton was waiting for the boys in the church office with a contract to be signed by them. Paul read it carefully, using his finger to follow the closely written lines. He explained the terms aloud to Josiah. They were the same as John Dyer had told them.

"Well, are you going to sign?" asked the sexton impatiently. "My dinner is getting cold."

John picked up the quill pen and signed his name, then handed the pen to Paul. For a few seconds, Paul waited. Then with a fine flourish which he had just learned at the Writing School, he signed his name. Josiah took the pen quickly. Slowly and with never a splutter, he added his name. The three other boys would sign later.

"You boys will like ringing these bells," said the sexton. "They're the best and sweetest in all America." He left then for his dinner.

The boys now climbed up the steep, narrow steps to the belfry to examine the bells. There were eight of them of different sizes and weights. They were shiny and smooth, for they were only three years old.

Paul read aloud the words cut in the largest bell. "We are the first ring of bells cast for the British Empire in North America."

A R., the initials of the maker, Abel Rudhall, and the date 1744 were also on the bells.*

"God preserve the Church of England," read Josiah on another.

"We'd better go now," said John.

"Let's look into the church before we leave," suggested Paul. He remembered how lovely Christ Church had been at Christmas time.

On tiptoes and whispering to each other, the boys went down the narrow steps and into the back of the church.

Square, high-walled wooden box pews with brass nameplates on their doors were on both sides of the aisle. Light flooded in from the clear-glass windows on the sides

---

* These same bells still hang in Christ Church, now known as the Old North Church.

and the big one in back of the altar. Brass chandeliers holding many candles hung from the ceiling.

A man in a long black robe with a lace robe over it came into the church and knelt in front of the altar. The boys were silent and wide-eyed. Paul felt uneasy. The devil and all his works were in a Church of England, his father had said. Paul almost expected to see a devil with a curling tail jump out from a dark corner.

The faint, harsh sound of the school bell came through an open window.

"It's one o'clock!" cried Paul in alarm.

Josiah groaned. "We've missed our dinner."

"Here's something to eat," offered John, pulling bread and cheese from his pocket.

"Come on, Paul," cried Josiah, grabbing the food.

Paul crammed a piece of cheese into his mouth. "I'm in for a beating now," he mumbled.

Going into Christ Church and skipping

38

dinner at noon! What would his father say to that?

CHAPTER 3

How Not to Get
a Beating

After school, Paul walked slowly across North Square to his home on Fish Street. At the head of Clark's Wharf was his father's small house and silversmith shop, which he rented from Doctor Clark. It was a good place for a silversmith. Merchants and sea captains who passed by could see the glittering pieces of silver in the small-paned shop window. If the sea captains had made a good voyage, they would often order a piece of silver.

The shop bell tinkled merrily as Paul opened the door. Mr. Revere and Jonah, his apprentice boy, were at work. The evening

41

sun glimmered on the tray Mr. Revere was polishing. He glanced up but only smiled at his son.

Paul quickly put on a leather apron and picked up a broom.

"Mind the bits of silver near the bench when you sweep," Mr. Revere called. "Jonah was filing a bowl today."

"I'm all ready for the gadroons," said Jonah, showing Paul the silver bowl.

Paul admired the piece. The gadroons were the curved flutings at the edge of a bowl. They were hard to make. "It's a perfect circle, Jonah," said Paul.

"Where were you at dinner time?" asked Mr. Revere.

Paul swallowed. He had hoped to be alone with his father when he told him where he had been and then took his punishment.

But Jonah interrupted just then. "Do you think the bowl is smooth enough to start making the gadroons, Mr. Revere?" he asked anxiously.

Mr. Revere ran his finger along the edge

of the bowl. "It's smooth enough," he said. "But wait until the morning to start. I want you to take these two spoons to Doctor Clark. Tell him they're the rent money for this month."

Doctor Clark lived in a brick house a few doors from the Reveres. Once, the Clark family had been wealthy and owned a fine house near North Square as well as their own wharf and shipyard. But they had lost their money. Their big house had been sold, and Thomas Hancock had bought the wharf and shipyard, though it was still called Clark's Wharf. However, Doctor Clark owned many small houses like the Revere's. Often his tenants gave him gifts for the rent instead of paying in cash.

Jonah quickly pulled off his leather breeches and smoothed his hair. "When Paul's your apprentice boy, Mr. Revere, he can wear my breeches," said Jonah. "They're still new on one side and only half worn on the other."

Paul put the breeches to his waist to measure them. All apprentice boys wore leather breeches like Jonah's. They were made very full so that they could be turned around when one side was worn from sitting. But Paul was too excited to pay much attention to the fit today. This was the first time he had heard that he was to be apprenticed to his father.

"Am I to be your apprentice boy, Pa?" he asked as soon as Jonah had left the shop.

Mr. Revere nodded. "You know almost as much as Jonah does now," he said. "And Master Hicks says you're doing well at the Writing School."

"I can read the Bible now without missing a word," said Paul proudly.

"You'll know enough arithmetic to keep my books with one more year at the Writing School," said Mr. Revere. "Jonah will have finished his time with me by then."

Paul knew all about the terms for an apprentice boy. Every tradesman and professional man had one or more boys helping him with his craft. The boy's parents or

other relatives paid the master a sum of money. The amount depended on the importance of the craft. For the money, the master would clothe, feed, and house the boy and teach him the trade, usually for seven years. If the apprentice could not learn the trade, he was returned to his parents. At the end of seven years, the master gave him a suit of clothes and signed his "freedom papers." These stated that he had served his time and could go into trade for himself. Since Paul would be apprenticed to his father, there would be no payment of money. Otherwise, the terms would be the same.

The last rays of the sun edged out of the two small-paned windows of the shop.

"Light the lamp, Paul," said Mr. Revere. "There's a bit more polishing I want to do."

Paul lit the lamp and moved it so that it would shine on his father's work. Mr. Revere looked up and nodded his thanks. "You still haven't told me why you weren't home for dinner," he said quietly.

Paul straightened up. The beating was

coming now, but at least Jonah was not in the shop. He glanced at the bunch of stout twigs that Mr. Revere used to punish his children. Paul wished he had put on Jonah's leather breeches. They were full and thick in the back.

"I was at Christ Church," he said. "I signed a contract to be a bell ringer."

"Christ Church! What's a son of mine doing among those idol worshipers!" cried Mr. Revere, almost dropping the tray. "God forgive you for the evil you have done this day."

"I was only in the belfry, Pa," said Paul quickly. He'd forgotten about going down into the church. "And I'll get two shillings a week for ringing the bells."

Mr. Revere rubbed his chin. "You're not hearing the sermons they preach? Or watching the heathens worshiping idols?"

"I won't see or hear anything, Pa," said Paul eagerly. "The walls of the belfry are so thick, I couldn't even hear the bells unless the windows were open."

47

He looked at his father. He was still frowning and had put down the tray.

"I'll be too busy waiting for my turn even to think about the devil and his works," added Paul.

The kitchen door next to the shop opened just then. Smells of freshly baked bread and hot spicy meat rushed into the room. Mrs. Revere stood in the doorway. "I've rabbit stew for supper," she called. "It will be

ready in a half hour." She turned to Paul. "Where were you at dinner time?"

But Paul quickly opened a cupboard and took out a silver band bracelet. "Look, Ma. I'm engraving your name and the Hitchbourn coat of arms on your bracelet."

His mother had been Deborah Hitchbourn. The men in her family were wealthy merchants and craftsmen. Paul knew that his mother was proud of her background and her relations.

"I'll be glad to show the bracelet to your Uncle Thomas, when next we invite him to dinner," she said, looking pleased. "Now wash up, and get ready for supper."

Mrs. Revere closed the door, and Paul and his father continued their work. Paul carefully drew a rectangle on the inside of the bracelet and printed REVERE within it. His father usually signed his pieces of silver P. REVERE.* Paul stared at the name in the bracelet for a moment.

"Ma says that Revere isn't our real name," said Paul. "Is that true?"

* See page 189.

"She's right," said Mr. Revere, his head bent over the tray. "My name was Apollos Rivoire when I first came to Boston in 1715. I was fourteen years old then."

"Why did you change your name to Paul Revere?"

"Because Boston people found 'Rivoire' hard to say, and I wanted to be successful in my trade."

"Riv-wahr," said Paul slowly, repeating his father's pronunciation. "That *is* hard to say." He picked up a small brush and passed it back and forth over his engraving. For a while there were only the sounds of work in the shop.

"Where did you come from, Pa?" Paul asked after a time. He had never questioned his father before this, though he knew something of his background. But now that Paul knew he was to follow in his father's trade, he thought he should know more about his father's family. Paul knew all about the Hitchbourns. Boston was full of them. All of Paul's brothers and sisters had been named for the Hitchbourns. Paul alone had a Rivoire name.

"I was born in a little village near Bordeaux (*bohr doh'*) in France," said Mr. Revere. "But when I was thirteen, my parents sent me out of the country because we were Protestants, and the King of France was putting people of our religion to death."

"Did you come to Boston then?"

"No. First I went to my Uncle Simon on the Island of Guernsey in the English Channel. He sent me to Boston. I wanted to be a silversmith."

"Who was your master in Boston?"

"John Coney, who had a shop near here on Anne Street. He was the finest silversmith in Boston. He learned his trade from Jeremiah Dummer, among others. So the silver pieces in this shop have the training of three generations of silversmiths in them, and you'll make a fourth."

Paul glowed at the words. He liked working with silver, and he knew his father was a fine craftsman.

"I was lucky to be able to come from a foreign country and in time to start a shop of my own," added Mr. Revere. "But there were many French Protestants who had come to Boston before I did. The Faneuils (*fan' 'ls*), and Bowdoins (*boh'd'ns*), and the Segournays (*sihg'er nihs*) were French Protestants. Our beliefs are like those of the English Puritans. Ours is the only true religion," said Mr. Revere firmly.

Paul sighed. His father's words could mean only one thing. Even going into another church was sinful, according to Mr. Revere. "I guess I'll have to take my beating and give up ringing the bells at Christ Church," thought Paul.

He smoothed the bracelet a last time and put it in the cupboard. "If you're going to beat me for signing the contract at Christ Church," said Paul to his father, "I wish you'd do it before supper. I can eat standing up."

Mr. Revere put the tray in the cupboard next to the bracelet. "I've no thought of beating you," he said mildly. "Ringing the bells in the belfry of Christ Church isn't like taking part in a service. And anyway, there's no sense in missing a chance to earn an honest penny."

Paul grinned happily. He was going to have the fun of ringing the bells, and get paid for his pleasure.

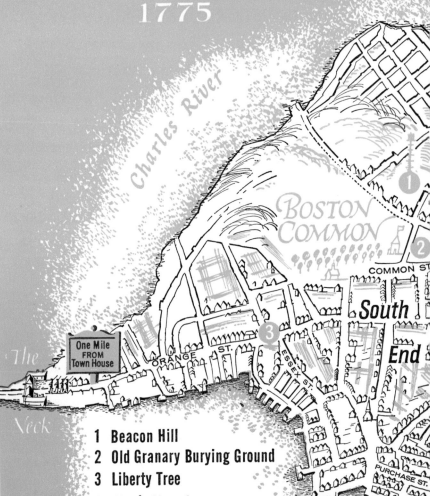

old Boston
1775

Charles River

BOSTON COMMON

COMMON ST.

South

End

One Mile FROM Town House

The

ORANGE ST.

ESSEX ST.

Neck

PURCHASE ST.

1 Beacon Hill
2 Old Granary Burying Ground
3 Liberty Tree
4 King's Chapel
5 Old South Meeting House
6 Town House

0   1/4   1/2 Mile

SHB

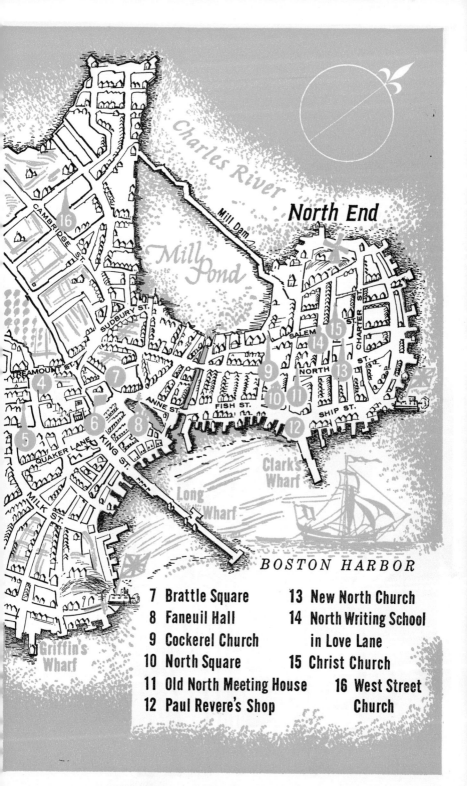

North End

Charles River

Mill Dam

Mill Pond

CAMBRIDGE ST.

TREAMOUNT ST.

SUDBURY ST.

SALEM ST.

CHARTER ST.

NORTH ST.

ANNE ST.

FISH ST.

SHIP ST.

QUAKER LANE

KING ST.

MILK ST.

Clark's Wharf

Long Wharf

Griffin's Wharf

BOSTON HARBOR

7 Brattle Square
8 Faneuil Hall
9 Cockerel Church
10 North Square
11 Old North Meeting House
12 Paul Revere's Shop
13 New North Church
14 North Writing School in Love Lane
15 Christ Church
16 West Street Church

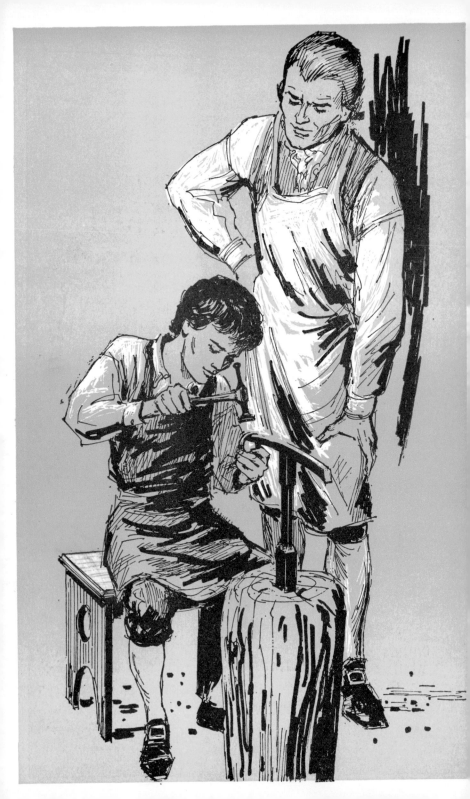

CHAPTER 4

A Silver
Sugar Bowl

Paul could not remember a time when he had not worked or watched in his father's silversmith shop. When he was very small, he had helped Jonah carry in the bags of willow-wood charcoal for the furnace. Later, he had been allowed to work the bellows until he knew just how much air to blow until the silver piece or sheet of metal that was being heated was a dull red.

After Paul was ten years old, it had been his morning task to fill the large earthen "pickling" vat with water and acid. He knew that when silver cooled after it had been heated, it had a gray film. Silversmiths called this a "fire scale." The silver was put into the vat then to make it bright again.

"Mind you put one part of acid to ten parts of water," Mr. Revere would caution Paul when he filled the vat. "And be sure to put the water in first."

Paul had no need of this warning after his first try. That time, he had added the water to the acid, and the hissing, spluttering mixture had blistered his hands and arms.

Bit by bit, Paul had learned each process in making a silver piece. Again and again, Mr. Revere repeated his instructions as Paul undertook a new task, for Mr. Revere was a good master. "Lightly, lightly now," he would call as Paul hammered and tapped on the silver. "And remember always to beat from the wrist."

When Paul prepared to solder his first piece of silver, his father watched with special care. "Be sure your edges are smooth before you begin to solder" was Mr. Revere's first instruction.

A solder mixture of silver, copper, and

zinc was used to join the pieces. First, however, the pieces must be filed perfectly so as to make a close fit. It was important, too, to have the right amount of heat when joining the edges, so that the solder would run clearly into the joint. Many a piece of silver with bumpy soldering was made by Paul, before he mastered this difficult task.

The first piece Paul had made by himself was the bracelet for his mother's birthday. He had melted the bracelet three times before he was sure it was a perfect circle. Over and over then, he had hammered the surface with his mallet until not a single hammer mark showed. He had been very proud to engrave it with his name.

Now Jonah was gone and Paul was apprenticed to his father. His fingers deftly handled tweezers, tongs, dividers, and shears. His wrists moved evenly and surely when he hammered. He had made porringers and tea strainers and other simple pieces by himself, and had helped his father make larger pieces. But everything Paul had made so far was from his father's design. Many times, however, he drew designs of pieces he would like to make by himself.

One day in late June when Paul was fifteen, Mr. Thomas Hutchinson came into the shop. The Hutchinsons lived near the Reveres in a fine mansion on the edge of North Square.

"Good morning, Revere," said Mr. Hutchinson pleasantly. Then he examined the tankard Mr. Revere was making. "That's a fine piece of work you are doing."

Mr. Hutchinson was a man of about forty. He was Speaker of the General Court, which was the lawmaking body in Massachusetts. He was also a member of Governor Bernard's Council.

Paul put aside his steel hammer and picked up his polishing cloth so he would not disturb the two men in their talk. For a time, they spoke about the war going on then in Europe and between the French and English colonies in America.

"We've fought the French now for sixty

years," said Mr. Hutchinson, "but if we don't drive them completely out of America, they will spread west of the mountains and hem us in."

"I am French-born," said Mr. Revere. "But I'd not like to see the King of France rule over America. We'd have no freedom of any kind."

Mr. Hutchinson put a small bag of coins on the counter. "I must be off to the Town House now," he said. "I came to order a silver sugar bowl. If I like the one you make, I'll order a whole new tea set to match the bowl."

"Have you any design for the bowl?" asked Mr. Revere.

"I want something rich and fanciful," said Mr. Hutchinson, "to fit in with the silver we already have."

Mr. Revere nodded. "I know what you mean," he said. Richly decorated pieces of silver were no longer the fashion, but some people liked such fancy work.

"Well, I must go now," said Mr. Hutchinson. He pointed to the bag of coins. "That should be enough for the sugar bowl and the fashioning. I made quite a profit from my last merchant ship, and I would like to use some of the silver."

Mr. Revere picked up the bag of coins and locked it in his cupboard. It was the custom for wealthy people to bring their money to a silversmith to have it made into some article. There were no banks in America in which to leave money. A piece of silver would be of less value to a robber than a bag of money. The silver pieces usually had the owner's initials as well as the maker's mark on them.

"I would like to make that sugar bowl, Pa," said Paul as soon as Mr. Hutchinson left the shop.

Mr. Revere looked startled. "But you've never made a sugar bowl by yourself."

"I've helped you with a dozen or more. I'm far ahead of the apprentices in other shops. You've said so yourself."

Mr. Revere rubbed his chin thoughtfully.

Paul watched anxiously. For a long time, he had been thinking of a design for a tea set, and his fingers itched to make the bowl.

"Well, go ahead," said his father at last. "We can melt it down, if you find the making too hard."

"I'll melt the silver now and be ready to work on it in the morning," said Paul, taking the bag of coins from the cupboard.

First he counted the silver and wrote down the amount in his father's account book. Then Paul dumped the coins into the melting pot, or crucible, as it was called. He added an extra bar of silver from his father's store so as to be sure to have enough. He made a record of this in the account book, too.

After the silver was melted, Paul added copper until he had nine and one-fourth parts silver and three-fourths copper. This was the standard set in England for sterling silver. Pure silver would be too soft to make into useful pieces.

When the mixture of silver and copper

63

was melted, Paul poured it into a skillet and waited until the metal was cold. Near the anvil, a fire of glowing charcoal was in a round iron tray screwed to a wooden support. In the tray were several bricks on which a piece of silver could be placed. In this way both heat and air could get to the metal.

Every now and then as Paul hammered on his sheet of silver to thin it, he paused and placed it on the bricks in the iron tray.

The silver became brittle when hammered, twisted, or rolled, and so it had to be softened by heat. Heating it from time to time was called "annealing." If the silver was not annealed while it was being worked, it would crack.

While the silver was on the bricks, Paul slowly turned the tray and gently blew the bellows. In this way, he kept the charcoal fire at a slow and even heat. As soon as the silver turned a dull red, Paul removed the sheet with his copper tongs. He waited a minute for the silver to cool, then plunged it into the pickling vat to remove the fire scale. When the sheet of silver was bright again, Paul continued to hammer. At last he thought the sheet of silver was thin enough to start the job of fashioning it into the sugar bowl.

For the next two days Paul was busy with pen and paper, compass and dividers as he drew the design for his sugar bowl. His father did not interrupt him to ask for help with other work in the shop. A new design was something creative, and he wanted his son to give every bit of his attention to his drawing.

Finally the drawing was finished. "My bowl will be pear-shaped and on a base," said Paul to his father as he studied the design.

Mr. Revere looked surprised. He himself was making a sugar bowl for Doctor Clark to pay for the rent. Mr. Revere's bowl was round-cheeked like an apple and richly decorated in a pattern of scrolls and leaves.

Doctor Clark also liked the old-fashioned designs in silver.

Paul put down his drawing. He knew what his father's look meant. After all, Mr. Hutchinson had said he wanted something "fanciful."

"If you don't like the design, Pa," said Paul, "I'll change it."

"Make the bowl as you see it, boy," said Mr. Revere. "You'll never be a true silversmith if you only copy."

Paul's eyes brightened. With his compass, he measured the circle for the bowl portion on his sheet of silver. The circle had to be wide, a little more than twice the number of inches of the height of the bowl. Carefully Paul cut the circle with his shears. The silver was brittle now, and Paul put it on the bricks in the hearth. He whistled softly as he watched the metal slowly turn red.

The days went by. Paul hammered, annealed, pickled, soldered, brushed, and polished. Gradually the sugar bowl took form. The bowl portion was shaped like a fat,

upside-down pear. In the middle was a band of engraving. Paul had first drawn the design for the band. Then he had cut the design into the metal with his engraving tools. The cover was plain, and had a shape that matched the narrow part of the base's pear. There was a silver pine cone on top. The bowl itself rested on a plain base. Altogether it was six inches high.

Once in a while, Mr. Revere checked what Paul was doing. "It needs to be a bit thinner here," he said once, "and smooth out those hammer strokes near the top." When the bowl was almost finished he said, "It doesn't have much decoration."

Paul flushed. "People in America are not as fancy as Londoners," he said. "We should use plainer things here."

But Paul was worried. The sugar bowl had taken nearly all of his time for almost two weeks. Suppose Mr. Hutchinson did not like it and his father lost the order for the whole tea set. He might lose other orders as well. There was little money coming into the shop these days. Paul felt that he should have helped his father with work that might bring in cash.

Finally the last bit of polishing on the sugar bowl was done. Paul held the bowl up to the window so that he could delight in its soft lights and shadows. Secretly, he continued to worry.

Next he weighed the sugar bowl and put

the amount on the bottom. Then Paul made a rectangle as he had done for his mother's bracelet. He printed in it, for a mark, the name REVERE.

"We'll take the bowl to Mr. Hutchinson after dinner," said Mr. Revere. "Put on your blue coat with the brass buttons. Be sure the buttons are shined, and mind you comb your hair."

Early in the afternoon, the Reveres crossed North Square to the Hutchinson house. Each carried a small leather bag. Paul knew the house well. He had even climbed the stone wall and peeped into the orchard and gardens, but he had never been inside. Next to the Hutchinson house was an even finer one that had been built by the Clarks. Now it was owned by Sir Harry Frankland, the Collector of the Port.

"We'll go to the kitchen entrance," said Mr. Revere. "The front door is not for the likes of us."

But as soon as the cook learned their errand, a serving boy brought the Reveres to another servant in the great entrance hall. "Master Hutchinson is in the library," said the man. "I'll take you to him."

Paul's eyes widened as the library door opened. He had never before seen such a grand room. The walls were paneled in wood. Thick rugs covered the floor. Richly carved furniture was everywhere. Velvet draperies hung at the long windows. A great glass chandelier glittered in the sunshine. Hundreds of books were on shelves reaching almost to the ceiling.

Mr. Hutchinson wore a waistcoat over his linen shirt. His unpowdered light-brown hair was tied back with a black ribbon. But he looked like an elegant gentleman even dressed in this simple way.

"I hope you will pardon my appearance," he said. "The day is quite warm, and I have been working on my manuscript." He pointed to a table covered with sheets of writing.

"Is that your history of Massachusetts, sir?" asked Mr. Revere. "Folks say you know

71

more about our colony and can write about it better than anyone."

Mr. Hutchinson looked pleased. "It is the first recorded history of Massachusetts," he said. "The first volume has been published, and now I am working on the second. But enough about my book. I believe you have brought me the sugar bowl I ordered."

Mr. Revere took the bowl from Paul's bag. "Is this to your liking, sir?"

Mr. Hutchinson looked a little surprised as he examined the bowl. Paul's heart began to pound. "He doesn't like it," he was thinking. "My father will lose the order." A heavy weight seemed to come down on Paul's shoulders. He had thought the sugar bowl so beautiful. And not one word had his father said to make him change his design.

Slowly Mr. Hutchinson turned the bowl over. "It is not like anything you have made for me, Revere," he said. "But I see you have put your name on the bottom and my initials and the weight, just as you always do."

"My father will tell him I have made the bowl," thought Paul. "No. I will tell him so myself." He straightened his shoulders and said. "I — "

But Mr. Revere put his hand on his son's shoulder. "The bowl was made in my shop," he said.

Paul gave his father a grateful look.

Mr. Revere opened his bag. "Would you

like this one better, sir?" He held out the
bowl he had made for Doctor Clark.

"But that was to pay our rent," thought
Paul. Still, it was better than to lose the
whole order. He knew his father was always
practical. He would be generous enough not
to let his son be blamed for a mistake, but
ready to save a situation if he could. The
weight that Paul felt eased a little. He

would work hard now to make up to his father for the loss of the rent.

"Oh, no. I prefer the first one," said Mr. Hutchinson.

Paul's heart was beating so happily, he could hardly breathe. His eyes shone as he watched Mr. Hutchinson examine the bowl.

"I shall want the whole tea set made like this one," said Mr. Hutchinson. "It is simple and has nice balance. People in America are like that. This sugar bowl is made for a colonial. My children will inherit it after me. And remember, my children and I are Boston-born and are proud of it."

Paul smiled widely. This was what he had tried to tell his father. But how much better Mr. Hutchinson had said it.

"The sugar bowl was made — " Mr. Revere started to say.

"The sugar bowl was made in the Revere shop," said Paul firmly, nudging his father.

Mr. Hutchinson smiled at Paul. "And perhaps you had something to do with the making," he said. He turned to Mr. Revere.

"Sell the other one to Doctor Clark," he added with a laugh. "He will think it much better than mine."

CHAPTER 5

Paul Revere—
Goldsmith

It's time for you to settle down and marry, Paul," said Mrs. Revere one early spring when Paul was twenty-two.

"Please don't talk to me now, Ma," said Paul. "I'm making a trade card."

He had said that only to avoid answering his mother. The design for the card was almost finished. He was engraving it for his friend Joseph Webb, an iron worker. Paul had drawn a fancy scrolled border with andirons and pots for decoration, and now he was listing the items that Joseph made and sold.

"The house is big enough for you to have

a wife," continued Mrs. Revere, paying no attention to Paul's request. "Your father would tell you the same. God rest his soul."

Mr. Revere had died two years before and was buried in the Old Granary Burying Ground with the Hitchbourns. Now Paul was master of the shop, with his brother Thomas for an apprentice.

"Paul Revere, Goldsmith," he wrote on his trade card. Even though Paul rarely made anything of gold but buckles, thimbles, and small frames, like other members of his craft he called himself a "goldsmith." This had been the trade name for the early workers in fine metals who worked in gold as well as silver.

"My father left a good name and seven children," Paul said firmly to his mother. "It's my job to provide for them."

"Some of them will be leaving soon. Deborah is to be married, and John will be apprenticed to a tailor. There's money enough made in this shop for you to support a wife," argued Mrs. Revere.

"What's in our kitchen besides stew pots, skillets, and sauce pans?" asked Paul, studying his card. It was hard to make his mother change a subject.

"A tea kettle," said his mother.

"A tea kettle, of course," said Paul, writing it on the card in large letters.

"And you're through with the wars, too," said Mrs. Revere, paying no attention to the change of subject.

"Thank Heavens for that," said Paul.

Soon after his father's death, Paul had enlisted in the Army. Most young men served at some time. England's wars against France seemed endless, and a fourth one had started in 1754. Paul had been made a second lieutenant. He had marched with his troops to Lake George and then back again, for there was no fighting. He had been happy to return to the smell of dried fish, tar, pitch, lumber, spices, and molasses that hung over Boston. He had done his duty for Massachusetts. He hoped he would never again have to go to war.

"You surely can afford a wife now," continued Mrs. Revere. "There's more work here than you and Thomas together can do."

Paul nodded. These were busy years for silversmiths. New England merchants were making money from the war, and they spent it freely for fine silver articles. Paul made his pieces simple in design. He had never forgotten the words of Thomas Hutchinson. Well-balanced pieces of silver with little decoration were best suited for colonials. Usually Paul's customers let him have his way, for he was fast becoming the best silversmith in Boston.

"I said you could afford a wife," repeated Mrs. Revere loudly, for her son had not answered her.

"But I haven't thought of a girl," he said.

"There's Sarah Orne," said Mrs. Revere. "Her family has money. And they are good church people."

"I'll think about it," said Paul. "Maybe she won't have me."

Mrs. Revere smiled and went back to her kitchen. She had little doubt that Sarah Orne would be pleased to marry her son. Paul was a fine-looking young man. He was sturdy and well-built, though not very tall. His dark skin, hair, and eyes made him stand out among the young men of the town, most of whom had blue eyes and light hair. He had a wide mouth and an easy, pleasant smile that showed his good teeth. He would be a hard-working, faithful husband, thought Mrs. Revere, just as her own husband had been. Sarah Orne would be a lucky girl if Paul decided to marry her.

The next Sunday, Paul went to the Cockerel Church with his mother and six brothers and sisters. He wore a new ruffled shirt and a green waistcoat embroidered by his mother with red oak leaves. The Ornes as well as the Hutchinsons also attended the Cockerel Church. It was called that because it had a great brass cock for its weathervane.

After the service, Paul walked home with Sarah, and the Reveres were all invited to dinner by Mrs. Orne. Sarah sat next to Paul at the table, but blushed and said scarcely a word during the meal. "She's a pretty little thing," thought Paul. "I'll take her rowing on the Charles next holiday."

With a little urging from his mother, Paul began to court Sara Orne. He walked home with her from church every Sunday. When the weather was warm, he took her rowing or to picnics. Sometimes he rented a one-horse carriage, and they went for a long ride or to a country dance.

On August 4, 1759, Paul and Sara were married. They lived with Paul's family in Mrs. Revere's house, which was only a little more crowded now. In the following spring, on April 3, the Reveres had their first child, a girl.

"We'll call her Debbie," said Paul. He did not want Sara to know that he was disappointed because his first child was not a boy.

But two years later, the Reveres did have a son. This time, Sara did the naming. "We'll call him Paul," she said.

Altogether they had eight children. Paul loved children, so was always happy when a new baby was born. The house would have been filled to bursting, if others in the household had not left. Deborah and Frances, Paul's oldest sisters, were married, and his brother John was apprenticed to a tailor.

Shortly after the birth of his son, Paul joined one of the political clubs in the North End. There were many such clubs now starting in Boston. The French and Indian War was over. England now owned all of North America east of the Mississippi. There were rumors that England would soon take strong control of the American colonies. Massachusetts was especially alarmed. Although it had an English royal governor, it governed itself in most ways.

Revere's club met in an old inn called the Salutation. In its smoke-filled rooms, the men drank ale and smoked their long-stemmed white clay pipes. They talked of their homes and work and politics.

Most of the men in Revere's club were tradesmen like himself, except for Doctor Joseph Warren. Paul took an instant liking to the blond, blue-eyed young doctor. As a physician, Joseph Warren had one quality that Paul Revere liked, although many Boston people thought it strange. Doctor Warren always insisted on washing his hands and instruments before treating a patient. "I want Joseph Warren to be our doctor," Revere told his family. "He'll take proper care of our little ones."

At times with Doctor Warren, Revere went to the Long Room over Edes and Gill's printing shop, where the *Boston Gazette* was published. Most of the club members had gone to Harvard College. But they welcomed Revere, although he was the only tradesman who came.

In this way, Revere grew to know James Otis, the great Boston lawyer, and Sam Adams, who seemed to control all the politics in the town. Revere listened respectfully to the speeches of James Otis, though at times his talk was wild.

Sam Adams was more to Revere's liking. He was about forty, with blue eyes and strong features. His clothes were shabby and often dirty, and his hands and head shook at times with palsy. But men listened to Sam Adams. He talked quietly and cheerfully, and had such charm of manner that he could get almost anyone to do his will.

Adams's father had been a brewer, and Sam had attended Harvard College. But he had failed at every business he had tried. He lived in a big shabby house on Purchase Street in the South End, near the docks. The workmen on the water front were devoted to him and would do anything he asked.

"Doesn't Mr. Adams have a trade or profession?" Revere asked Doctor Warren.

"Sam's trade is politics," said Warren with a laugh. "He doesn't want to hold office himself, but he likes to pull strings so that the men he believes are best will be elected."

Early in February, 1764, cases of smallpox were reported in Boston. By the end of the month, Debbie, the Revere's oldest child, was ill with the disease.

"Do you want her taken to the pesthouse?" asked Doctor Warren.

The pesthouse was the building to which people were taken who had a disease that was "catching." It was dirty, with few comforts or proper care for the patients.

"I'll not have my little Debbie taken to that dreadful place," said Revere. "We'll nurse her at home."

"Then we'll have to put up a warning flag

and have a guard in front of the house," said Doctor Warren. "You will be kept in, you know, and will have no trade."

Revere nodded. He knew what the loss of trade would mean. Times were getting hard, now that the big money from the war was no longer made.

In a month, Debbie was cured, and Revere opened his shop. But it was the end of May before the smallpox was ended in Boston and men began to meet again. Revere was glad to spend his evenings once more with his political club, for there was not much work in the shop. He had rented part of it to Joseph Webb.

Much had happened during the months that smallpox had kept people from meeting. Word had come from England that Parliament expected the colonists to help pay what England owed from the war, as well as the cost of ten thousand soldiers to be sent to protect America against the Indians. The money was to come from a Stamp Tax.

"We've paid our share, both in men and in

89

money," said one of the men at the Salutation. "We helped to win the war."

"And why should we need British soldiers to protect us now?" asked another. "The French are gone, and we've always been able to protect our borders from Indian attacks."

Revere listened but said little. He was never very good at talking, though he shared the views of the others.

"What is this Stamp Tax?" he asked Doctor Warren later.

"It's a stamp we'll have to buy to put on newspapers and some other papers. Its price will differ according to the importance of the paper."

"Has Parliament the right to make us pay a tax?"

Revere had never paid taxes to England, except customs duties when he received goods from England.

"They haven't the right according to John Adams. He's a young lawyer from Braintree, a cousin of Sam Adams's," said Warren. "John wrote a piece for the *Gazette* about the tax. He said we shouldn't be taxed unless we have people from the colonies in Parliament. No colony has elected anyone to Parliament."

"What do Bernard and Hutchinson say?" asked Revere.

Sir Francis Bernard was the Royal Governor, and Thomas Hutchinson was now the Lieutenant Governor of Massachusetts. The feeling of the people of Massachusetts had changed toward Thomas Hutchinson since Revere was a boy. They felt he was too greedy for public office. Not only did he hold his old offices as well as that of Lieutenant Governor, but he was also a judge in two kinds of courts. In addition, he saw that his relatives had good positions.

"Both of them say they have written letters against the tax to Parliament," said Warren. "But Hutchinson has named his brother-in-law, Andrew Oliver, to be the Stamp Tax collector."

"Tommy-Skin-and-Bones Hutchinson takes care of his own," said Revere bitterly. This was the nickname Thomas Hutchinson now had in Boston.

There had been no orders on Revere's books from the Hutchinsons these last few years. It was well-known to the Lieutenant Governor that the men in the political clubs were against him, and Revere made no secret of his club membership.

The men in all the political clubs met more often now. Sam Adams brought his cousin John, though he was not a member, to the meetings in the Long Room over Edes and Gill's printing shop. John was thirteen years younger than Sam. He lived in Braintree but had his office in Boston. Revere enjoyed listening to John Adams at the meetings. He was short and plump, with a round face and high color. He was a good talker who came to the point without the rush of words one heard so often from James Otis.

One evening, Sam Adams brought John Hancock to the Salutation when Revere and Doctor Warren were at a table. Hancock was a small man, somewhat stoop-shouldered, but very richly dressed. Thomas Hancock had died in August and left his fortune to his wife Lydia. John lived with her in their great mansion on Beacon Hill and would inherit the business and fortune when she died. He would be one of the richest men in New England then.

Revere had not seen John Hancock very often in the years when they were both growing up. However, Hancock had not forgotten that when he was a small boy, Paul Revere had come to his aid. Hancock was always friendly when they met and, as his uncle had, ordered pieces of silver from the Revere shop. He greeted Revere, then moved to another table with Sam Adams.

"What is John Hancock doing in this club?" Revere asked Doctor Warren. Revere knew that most of the rich merchants sided with the party of the Royal Governor.

"Sam Adams won him over to our side," said Warren with a grin. "We need Hancock's money for our cause."

In May, 1765, the news came to Boston

that the Stamp Act had been passed and would go into effect on November 1, 1765. On August 14, a stuffed body dressed like Andrew Oliver was hung from the tallest elm on the corner of Orange* and Essex Streets. The tree was said to be one hundred and twenty years old. Under its spreading branches and those of nearby trees, a thousand people could gather. Men had been meeting at the corner since the first news of the Stamp Tax, and they now called the tall elm the Liberty Tree.

Late in the afternoon of that same day, Revere was one of about fifty men who took down the stuffed body and carried it in a funeral march to the Town House. "Liberty, property, and no stamps," they chanted as they marched.

After the march, Revere went home. But a mob which wanted only an excuse for a fight raced along King Street pulling down fences and signs. They ended by breaking

* Now Washington Street.

into Andrew Oliver's house and doing a great deal of damage. From that day on, there were small acts of mob violence almost every day.

It was very hot on the night of August 26, 1765, and Revere tossed restlessly in bed. Suddenly he sat up. The faint sound of whistles, drum beats, yells, and clumping of boots which had half-awakened him were heard now under his window. In a minute, he had pulled on his breeches and was running down the narrow stairs.

"I'll see what's happening," he cried to Sara. "Close the shop after me, and tell Thomas to watch. There's trouble on the streets."

Revere ran across North Square. Other men were also running. A great crowd was gathered around the house of Thomas Hutchinson. There was the sound of tinkling glass as stones were thrown through the lighted windows of the dining room and kitchen. Men were climbing over the garden walls. More were at the entrance door battering it with axes. Above the howls of the mob, Revere heard what had happened.

Both North and South End mobs were there. They had broken into several big houses on their way to North Square and had emptied the wine cellars.

"They're in a dangerous state. . . . Nothing can stop them. . . . Hutchinson's being paid back now for backing the Stamp Tax," cried those who watched.

"I'm going back home," said one after another of the bystanders. But Revere stayed on for a time.

The mob was in Hutchinson's house now. All sorts of things were being thrown through the windows. Broken furniture, portraits, china, pieces of silver, and rugs were tossed outside. Men were on the roof, tearing at the gutters and the slates. Others were picking up things that had been thrown outside and were hurrying away.

Soberly, Revere went home. Was this the way Boston was to show it was against the Stamp Tax? At dawn, he was out on the street again. He stared in horror at Thomas Hutchinson's great house, which had been one of the finest in Massachusetts. He remembered the beauty of the library. The doors of the house swung open now. The broken windows blinked in the rising sun. The fence around the house was ruined.

Revere saw Hutchinson's friend Andrew Eliott, of nearby New North Church, picking up mud-stained sheets of paper in the street. Revere remembered the manuscript he had seen on that long-ago visit when he was a boy. "This is the first recorded history of Massachusetts," Mr. Hutchinson had said then. These must be pages from the second volume he was writing.*

All that day Revere heard news of what had happened. The Hutchinson family had been at home eating a late supper when the attack had begun. Everyone except Thomas Hutchinson had fled to the nearby house of Hutchinson's sister. Then his little daughter Sally had come back for him and said that

* This mud-stained manuscript is now in the Massachusetts Historical Society.

she would not leave without him. With that, he, too, had gone.

The men in Revere's club were serious that night. The leading people of Boston were ashamed of what had happened. Even Sam Adams thought the attack had been an outrage.

"A mob like that only wants to destroy and steal," said Doctor Warren. "We'll not win our cause that way."

"A mob like that could do us good, if it were controlled and trained," said Sam Adams thoughtfully.

Revere looked at Sam Adams. Was that what he planned?

Boston was not the only place in which the people were against the Stamp Act. Patrick Henry led the fight against it in Virginia. A Stamp Act Congress was called to meet in New York. Nine of the colonies chose men to send to it. This was the first time so many colonies had acted together in a cause.

"We'll not buy or sell English goods until the law is repealed," the members agreed.

The Stamp Act went into effect on November 1, 1765, but not a single stamp was sold in any colony. Revere was with the Sons of Liberty when they forced Andrew Oliver, the stamp collector, to meet them under the Liberty Tree. "I swear never to sell a stamp," Oliver solemnly promised.

In the spring of 1766, the Stamp Act was repealed. The merchants of England had lost too much money when the colonists refused to trade with them.

The news of the repeal came to Boston on May 19. Guns boomed from Castle Island, church bells rang, and the Liberty Tree was hung with flags and banners. In the evening, hundreds of people hung lighted lanterns on the tree.

Revere had learned copper engraving, and he made a copper plate to celebrate the event. "To every lover of liberty," he engraved upon it.

CHAPTER 6

The Boston
Massacre

Revere was engraving a silver teapot when John Singleton Copley, the portrait painter, came into the shop.

"I've finished your silver picture frame, Mr. Copley," said Revere. "I'll get it for you."

"This is nice," said Copley, examining the frame. "How much do I owe you?"

Revere checked his account book and wrote out a bill.

"I'd like to paint your portrait instead of paying for the frame," said Mr. Copley.

"Paint me?" Revere was astonished.

"Yes, if you'd like that."

Revere grinned a little. "I've never thought of having my portrait painted. But Sara and the children would like it. And so would my mother. Her folks, the Hitchbourns, have always had their portraits painted." Then he frowned a little. "But you'd be losing money." He knew that Copley was paid fifteen pounds for a half-length portrait. He was so busy and had made so much money that he now owned a house and big piece of land on Beacon Hill.

"Sometimes I paint for my pleasure rather than to fill my purse," said Copley.

"I'll finish this bit of engraving and then change into my Sunday coat," said Revere. He had seen some of the portraits Copley had painted. The sitters were important people. They wore velvet coats, lace ruffles, and powdered wigs. Even Sam Adams had put on his best coat and powdered his hair for his portrait by Copley.

"Don't change," said Copley. "I want to paint you as you are, engraving that teapot. I'll make a sketch now."

Revere shrugged his shoulders. He wasn't quite sure that Sara and the children would like a portrait of him painted in his work clothes.

In an hour, the artist rolled up his sketching paper. "I'll drop by on another day when you are working," he said.

It was a month before Revere's portrait was finished, for Copley was a careful artist and usually required many sittings before he was satisfied.

"It's just as if I were looking into a mirror," said Revere in wonder when he had his first look.

Mr. Copley had painted him in his full-sleeved white linen shirt and sleeveless woolen jacket. The tools he used were on the table. He was looking straight out, his chin in one hand and the teapot resting on the engraving cushion in the other. He looked as if he had just stopped working to talk. His dark eyes were thoughtful, and there was a bit of a smile on his wide, firm mouth.

"We'll hang it in the bedroom," said Sara

107

when she was shown the portrait. "I'll not have it all smoked up from the kitchen fire."

Only Revere's mother was disappointed. "My grandfather, Captain Richard Pattishall, wore a velvet coat and lace ruffles for his portrait," she said.

Shortly after Revere's portrait was painted, John Baker, the surgeon dentist of Boston, announced that he planned to leave the town.

"I'm going to have John Baker teach me his trade before he leaves," Revere told Doctor Warren. "I'll have a way of making extra money when there's not much work in silver."

On September 19, 1768, Revere put an advertisement in the *Boston Gazette*. "Whereas many Persons are so unfortunate as to lose their Fore-teeth by Accident, and otherways, to their great Detriment not only in Looks but speaking both in Public and Private: — This is to inform all such that they may have them replaced with artificial ones, that looks as well as Natural, & answers the End of Speaking to all intents, by PAUL REVERE, Goldsmith, near the Head of Dr. Clark's Wharf, Boston."

In time, one of Revere's customers was Doctor Warren. "I've lost my eye tooth and the one next to it," he said. "Can you make me two that will fit? I have trouble when I have to make a speech."

"You'll not be able to chew with the ones I make for you," said Revere. "But you will look more natural, and will be able to speak better."

He examined Warren's mouth and the next day had whittled two teeth out of the tusk of a hippopotamus. "Ivory would turn yellow," he told his patient. "Now open your mouth. I'll fasten each tooth to the one next to it with the silver wire I make in my shop."

In a half hour, Doctor Warren was looking into a mirror and grinning widely.

"If they get loose, come back and I'll

tighten them," said Revere. "I'll soon be able to make teeth you can chew with."

In 1768, Parliament passed the Townshend Acts. These put a tax on tea, glass, lead, and painters' colors.

"We'll not buy English goods," said the colonists. "That's the way we made Parliament repeal the Stamp Tax."

The merchants were not concerned at first about the law. They thought they would be able to smuggle English goods. It was not very hard for a merchant to have a cargo delivered by a Dutch ship. The coast line of America was long and not well-guarded by the English customs officers.

But this time the British planned to use force to end the smuggling. In October, Revere was in the crowd on King Street that silently watched two regiments of British troops march toward the Town House.

With the coming of the soldiers, Revere was busy in his shop, for the British officers ordered pieces of silver. He also had a good sale of copper plates showing the harbor of

Boston. One showed the landing of the British troops.

"I think by now we can afford to live in a house of our own," Revere said to his family in the beginning of 1770. "I have over two hundred pounds saved, and Captain John Erving has a good house for sale in North Square."

Even old Mrs. Revere was pleased with the idea. Her son had six children now, all girls except for young Paul. The lad was ten, and he worked in the silver shop with his father. It was about time they had a home of their own.

In February, Revere bought Captain Erving's house. It was a good frame house, though it was nearly a hundred years old. It had two stories. The second story overhung the street. Its front was on the street, and its small-paned windows were protected by heavy wooden shutters. Downstairs were a parlor and kitchen, and upstairs were the bedrooms.

After he had been in the house about a

year, Revere built a barn and bought a brown mare. He loved to ride, and up to this time had always had to borrow or hire a horse.

The Reveres were delighted with their house in North Square (which really was not a square, but a triangle). It was only a block from the water front. There was always the bustle of people about. There were a town pump, a market, and a guard house in the square. Around the sides of the square were small houses and shops, built right up to the street, all clean and well-kept. Some had tiny fenced yards on the side. Most of them had shop signs instead of numbers, but Revere still kept his silver shop at the head of Clark's Wharf.

Bells sounded all day long in North Square — market bells, shop bells, the bell of the town crier, and sweetest of all, the bells of Christ Church, which was not far away. At one end of the square was the Old North Meeting House, but the Reveres still attended the Cockerel Church, which was behind their house. Just off the edge of the square lived Thomas Hutchinson. His house was now repaired and again the residence of the Lieutenant Governor. The only drawback to life in the square, or anywhere else in Boston, was the presence of the British troops.

"We'll not give the soldiers lodging," the people of Boston had said when the troops arrived. Not even General Gage, the commander of all the British troops in America, could force the citizens to take the soldiers into their homes.

Some of the troops were camped on the

Common or in Brattle Square. Others were housed in empty sail lofts or warehouses. The beat of their drums, the clumping of their boots, the shrill commands of their officers were heard from dawn until dusk. Small boys threw rocks when the soldiers weren't looking and yelled, "Lobster back!" or "Bloody back!" or strutted in imitation of the marching men.

"Keep the children off the street," Revere warned his wife. "There will be trouble in Boston some day."

There was a heavy snowfall on March 5, 1770, but by evening the snow had ended, and a full moon shone on the clean white streets. Revere was in his shop annealing a sheet of silver while young Paul worked the bellows.

At nine o'clock, church bells began ringing from all directions. "There's a fire somewhere!" cried Revere, pulling on his cloak and grabbing his leather fire bucket. "Lock the shop and bank the furnace," he called to his son and ran into the street.

115

Outside Revere glanced at the sky. There was no red glow or sign of smoke. Other people were in the street, all running toward the center of town.

"What's happened?" cried Revere.

He caught only a few words in answer. "King Street — Soldiers — Sentry."

Suddenly there was a crackling sound of gunfire. Revere stopped abruptly. Others in the street did the same. Then came shrill whistles and the cry, "Town-born turn out! Town-born turn out!" It was the dreaded signal of the Sons of Liberty.

Revere threw his fire bucket into a doorway. It would probably be safe, for it was plainly marked with his name. With long strides, he ran toward King Street. Others went with him, but some went indoors.

A great crowd was in King Street in the square on which the Town House faced. There was hushed horror in their faces. People spoke in low voices.

"What's happened here?" asked Revere, as he pushed his way to the front.

He heard bits of news as he moved forward. A lone British sentry had been posted in front of the Town House. A crowd had gathered and thrown chunks of ice and coal and shouted insults at him. The sentry had replied in the same way and had dared the crowd to attack him. He had been pushed back, then had called for help. Captain Preston, the officer of the day, and seven soldiers had rushed to the sentry's aid.

"Why did the British shoot? Who gave the order?" asked Revere.

No one knew who had given the order to shoot, he was told. Suddenly there had been a blaze of gunfire from the British. Four of the colonists had been killed at once. Others had been wounded.

There was too much noise now to hear more of the story. The rallying cry of the Sons of Liberty had brought more onlookers. Revere now had a forward place. He saw John Adams standing near him. Both stared in horror at what they saw. Great splashes of blood were on the snow. Men were picking up the bodies of those who had fallen. The crowd made an aisle for the bearers. With their cloaks, others were covering the bodies that lay very still in the snow.

Now men were waving sticks, muskets, fire shovels, iron rods, or whatever they held in their hands. "It was murder! . . . It was a bloody massacre! . . . Let's burn their barracks!" was being shouted all around.

Revere saw John Adams pull down his hat and push his way out of the crowd. The Adamses were living in Boston now, about two blocks from the Town House. "He's afraid for his family," thought Revere.

On the steps of the Town House knelt Captain Preston and the eight soldiers, their guns in position to fire. Drums were rolling now, and the clatter of heavy boots sounded. In a few seconds the whole square was surrounded by soldiers. All quickly dropped to their knees and readied their guns to fire.

"There's Hutchinson!" someone shouted. "Up in the balcony!"

Revere looked up to the little balcony out-

side the council chamber on the second floor of the Town House. Thomas Hutchinson, his wig and hat crooked, his lace ruffles pushed halfway around his neck, stood there with arms outstretched. Governor Bernard had left for England the year before, and Hutchinson now governed Massachusetts.

The noise of the crowd died a little. "Go home, everyone. Let the law settle this thing!" shouted Hutchinson. "I'll see that Captain Preston and the soldiers are put in jail this night, and brought to trial at once. I promise you."

"And remember it was murder, Governor," called someone. "They should be hanged."

"It was a bloody massacre!" came the cry everywhere.

☆ ☆ ☆

As soon as the sun was up the next morning, Revere was back at the square. A sentry shivered in front of the Town House entrance, but no one else was there. No fresh

snow had fallen. There were ruts and foot-
prints everywhere, but patches of blood still
showed near the Town House steps.

Quickly Revere made a rough sketch of
what had happened. He drew in the Town
House and the buildings that lined the
square. Crude sprawling figures showed the
position of the men who had been killed.
Two were near the soldiers. One was far-
ther away, and another in Quaker Lane.
Letters indicated their names. Revere
worked carefully. The Sons of Liberty
would want this actual record of what had
happened.

About noon, Revere was one of the group
of fifteen headed by Sam Adams who called
on Governor Hutchinson in the council
chamber. This was the first time Revere
had been in the room, and he was a little
awed. It was a great square chamber with
deep fireplaces and a glittering chandelier.
On opposite walls were large portraits
framed in gold of James II and Charles II,
with their ermine-edged robes sweeping the

floor. The Governor and his council sat in high-backed chairs around a handsome table.

The group, said Sam Adams quite firmly, asked that the Governor remove the troops from Boston.

"I have no authority to give orders to the King's troops," said Governor Hutchinson. "But I will remove one regiment to Castle Island."

Back to the crowd waiting at the Old South Meeting House went Sam Adams and his committee.

"Is it the town's wish that one regiment be removed?" he shouted. "Or shall it be both regiments or none?"

"Both regiments or none!" roared the crowd.

Once more the group went to the council chamber. "If you can remove one regiment, sir, you can remove both," said Sam Adams to the Governor. "We will not be responsible for what happens in this town, if the troops are not withdrawn."

Revere saw Hutchinson grow pale. "He's

remembering the night the mob attacked his house," he thought.

The Governor leaned over and talked in whispers to Colonel Dalrymple, who was in command of the British troops in Boston. Then Hutchinson gave a stiff nod to Sam Adams. "Tell the people that both regiments will be removed."

There was little talk in Boston that day except about what had happened in King Street. Four men had been killed and a number wounded. Patrick Carr, an innocent bystander, had been badly wounded and would surely die. Captain Preston and the soldiers were in jail.

"Will they be tried soon?" Revere asked Doctor Warren.

"The trial may be delayed. The soldiers managed to get John Adams and Josiah Quincy for their lawyers."

Revere was shocked. "But they are both good Whigs. Why are they defending the British soldiers?"

By this time, the citizens of the colonies

were in two political parties, as they were in England. Those who believed the King had the right to rule called themselves Tories, as they did in England. Those who believed Parliament should control the government and who also wanted representatives from the colonies in Parliament were called Whigs, as they were in England.

"No other lawyers would take the case," said Doctor Warren in answer to Revere. "John Adams said that in a free country like ours, every man accused of a crime should have a lawyer to defend him."

Revere shook his head. He thought John Adams was an honest man, and probably the best lawyer in Massachusetts. But this was like treason to the Whig cause. "It was a bloody massacre," said Revere. "I can't understand John Adams."

By the end of three weeks, Revere had an engraving ready for sale. He did not try to be as correct in the details as in the rough sketch he had made the morning after the massacre. The engraving was meant to sell and keep the memory of the massacre alive.

In this new drawing, fire blazed and clouds of smoke came from the guns of a line of British soldiers. Men, dead and dying, lay sprawled on the ground. Close to the soldiers was a crowd of citizens, all very quiet and harmless-looking. The Town House and the buildings on both sides of the street were drawn in full detail. "Engraved Printed and Sold by Paul Revere" was on the bottom. The prints sold as fast as Revere could make them.

The trial of the British soldiers was delayed until late in October. By that time, the tempers of the people of Boston had cooled. The leaders were anxious that the world should think the attack on the sentry had been made by a mob instead of the good citizens of the town. But even most of the leaders still thought that the men who died had been murdered.

Revere went to the trial as often as he could. Each time, the gallery of the courtroom was filled. The four judges who heard the case wore their crimson robes, since the prisoners were accused of murder. The soldiers, dressed in their red uniforms, made a blaze of color on the bench.

During the months since the massacre, the two defense lawyers had examined nearly a hundred witnesses. They hoped to prove that the soldiers had fired in self-defense. Their best witness was Patrick Carr.

Patrick Carr had lived in great pain for four days. Before he died, he had given a statement to the doctor who had attended him. "I bear no grudge against the soldiers," Patrick had told the doctor. "They fired in self-defense."

On the last day of October, Captain Preston was declared "Not guilty as charged." About six weeks later, the soldiers, who had been tried separately, also were freed. Two who were proved to have fired were branded in their hands for punishment.

Revere went slowly out of the courtroom with the crowd when the branding was over. It was almost dark by then. He was glad the trial was over. There were rumors that the Townshend Acts would be repealed.

"We'll have peace, now that the soldiers are gone, and business should be good," thought Paul Revere.

CHAPTER 7

"Boston Harbor Is a Teapot!"

The evening was warm for early June, but Paul Revere hurried home. Ever since Sara had died in the spring, he had tried to be with the children at supper time. A nurse took care of Isanna, the new baby, and Revere's mother tried to manage the other children. But the house always seemed to be in an uproar, with the constant crying of the baby loudest of all.

Revere lifted his hat to Rachel Walker, who was coming out of her great-aunt's house near his own. She was a well-dressed young woman with thick, dark hair, a sloping forehead, and a rather long nose.

"Rachel's a nice girl," thought Revere. "I wonder why she has never married." He knew she came from a good family and had been well-educated. "She must be about twenty-seven now," he guessed, for he had known her since she was a child.

"I heard the baby is not so well since poor Sara died," said Rachel. "I've brought some herbs to make a tea for her and some cookies for the children." She pointed to the basket on her arm covered with a fresh white napkin.

Revere's face brightened. "The children will be glad of that. They've not had much that's special since Sara died. My mother's getting old, you know."

As he opened the door of his house for Rachel, the shrill noise of children's voices and his mother's scolding tones filled the air.

Revere grinned at Rachel. "You see what I mean," he said.

An hour later, Revere sat at the head of his supper table spread with a fresh cloth, and with clean-washed children about him.

130

His mother sat comfortably at the other end of the table. Rachel moved back and forth from fireplace to table.

"This is the most peace we have had in many a month," said Mrs. Revere. "I hope you'll be coming often, Rachel."

"I will. I love the children," she answered.

Rachel and Paul were married on September 23, 1773. Soon all the tangled strings of the Revere household were gathered in Rachel's capable hands. A month after his second marriage, Revere stood with a group reading a poster nailed to the side of the Town House.

"Friends! Brethren! Countrymen! That worst of plagues, the detested tea, is arrived," he read. "Every friend to his country is now called upon to meet at Faneuil Hall at nine o'clock this day. The bells will give the signal." The poster was dated "Nov. 29, 1773."

The ship *Dartmouth* had brought the tea the day before from England. Parliament had passed a new law to keep the British

131

East India Company from going bankrupt. The company would be allowed to ship its tea directly to America without paying the tax in England.

"The tea from England should be cheaper now than the tea that is smuggled in from Holland," said a woman who stood next to Revere.

"But we'll have to pay a three-penny tax here on each pound that we buy," he said, frowning at her.

The woman looked puzzled. "Then what should we do?"

"Not let the *Dartmouth* unload her cargo," answered Revere.

Just then the bell in the Old South began to ring, and he hurried to the meeting. The hall was already full, and plans were quickly agreed upon. Mr. Rotch, the owner of the *Dartmouth*, was to be told he could not unload his ship. Each night, twenty-five men were to watch the harbor to see that the order was carried out. Revere and five other men were chosen to ride to neighboring seaports to warn the people that tea ships might try to unload at their wharves.

Revere's horse was a sturdy brown mare with a blaze of white on its forehead. It could go fifty or sixty miles a day, if needed. Sam Adams had chosen Revere to be an express rider to take messages for the patriots of Boston. "He can be trusted, and he's a good rider," Sam told the leaders.

Sam Adams had started the system by which the colonies were kept informed. A group of men in each colony wrote letters telling what was happening in their colony to the same kind of group in other colonies. They were called Committees of Correspondence. The system kept the colonies united as well as informed.

Revere also took his turn at watch. The *Dartmouth* was tied up at Griffin's Wharf with its cargo still unloaded. Soon two other ships, also loaded with tea, joined the *Dartmouth* at Griffin's Wharf.

Each day feeling mounted in Boston. In twenty days, the *Dartmouth* would have to be unloaded, or its cargo would be seized by the customs officers and sold at auction. Mr. Rotch pleaded with Governor Hutchinson for permission to send the *Dartmouth* back to England with the tea. But the Governor refused.

On the evening of December sixteenth, thousands of people crowded into the Old South Meeting House and the streets outside. They were waiting for Mr. Rotch to return from a final meeting with Governor Hutchinson.

Revere stood near the doorway of the meeting house. He held a red blanket and a pot of soot. Plans had been made for what was to be done that night. Candles were being lit now in the meeting house, for it was nearly six o'clock. He could see Sam Adams standing in the wide pulpit in front, and Josiah Quincy making a speech from the balcony.

There was an uproar outside. "Mr. Rotch is here! Mr. Rotch is here!" was shouted.

Somehow room was made for the young

ship owner to push his way to the front of the meeting house.

"The Governor has refused," he cried up at Sam Adams. "He says the ship must be unloaded. What would you have me do?" added Rotch in despair.

But Sam Adams paid no attention to the pleas of the ship owner. "This meeting can do nothing more to save the country!" Sam shouted, and immediately left the pulpit.

Sam's words were the signal. Revere pushed and elbowed his way through the crowd and raced along the streets to the Green Dragon Tavern.

"Salt-water tea! . . . Boston harbor's a teapot tonight! . . . To Griffin's Wharf!" he heard the shouts as he ran.

Men and boys at the Green Dragon Tavern were smearing their faces with soot, sticking feathers in their hair, and wrapping themselves in blankets. Most of them swung hatchets to their shoulders as they formed in line and marched to Griffin's Wharf.

The streets and water front were already

crowded with people. Other men in rough Indian dress were coming from Edes and Gill's printing shop. In the bright moonlight, the three ships tied up at the wharf could be plainly seen.

"Me know you!" Revere grunted the password to Lendall Pitts, the son of a wealthy merchant and the leader of the group in front of the *Dartmouth*. More "Indians" were gathering near the other two ships.

Up the gangplank of the *Dartmouth* strode the men. There was no protest from the mate who handed Lendall Pitts the keys and sent a cabin boy for lights.

Down in the hold, Revere helped to lift a chest of tea to the deck. Others were doing the same. Hatchets gleamed in the moonlight on deck, as the chests were broken open. The water splashed high as chests and tea were dumped overboard. The men worked grimly. There was not even a shout from the people on the wharf as the first chest went tumbling over.

The sky was pale gray with streaks of rose. The last of the chests bobbed in the water. The work on the other ships was finished as well. Then the men on board began to laugh and talk a little. It was as if something had been lifted from their shoulders. Down the gangplank, Revere strode with the rest. A fife began to play. A drum was beaten. With hatchets on their shoulders, the men marched toward the Town House.

As they passed the Coffin House Tavern, a window was opened and a man stuck out his night-capped head. "Well, boys," he shouted, "you've had a fine evening for your Indian caper. But mind, you'll have to pay the fiddler."

It was Admiral Montague, the commander of the British fleet. Revere recognized his voice.

"Never mind, Squire!" shouted Lendall Pitts. "Come on down now, and we'll settle the bill."

The window went down with a bang.

At home, an hour later, Revere came into

the kitchen, where Rachel was serving porridge to the children.

"Pa's an Indian!" screamed Debbie, the oldest girl, looking a little frightened.

"Don't be afraid," said her father with a grin. "I've just been making salt-water tea." He moved over to Rachel and kissed her. "I'll eat my porridge now," he said, "and then be off to bed."

Two hours later, a messenger pounded at the door of the Revere house with a batch of letters from the Committee of Correspondence. Revere was to ride to New York and Philadelphia with the story of what had happened.

Young Paul saddled his father's horse while he made ready.

"What do you suppose the other colonies will do?" asked Rachel, who knew all that had happened.

"We'll find out soon," said her husband. He quickly kissed her good-by.

How lucky he was to have married someone like Rachel, thought Revere as he galloped along the Post Road. She was a good mother to the children and kept the house well. She understood and was interested in what her husband was doing in his political club. She even argued with him sometimes. "Rachel keeps me from being too sure of myself," thought Paul.

About five months after the "tea party" in Boston, the citizens were told the way in which they would be punished. The port of Boston was to be closed completely after June 1, 1774. Salem rather than Boston was to be the capital. Governor Hutchinson was to go to London to make a report, and in his absence General Gage, the commander of the British troops in America, was to be the governor. British regiments under Gage were to keep order. They were to live in the houses of the citizens.

The people of Boston were stunned when they learned the new orders. "There is no justice in these laws," said their leaders. "They have been made only to punish us."

Even the timid ones agreed now that while England might have the right to tax them, these new laws had been passed only for revenge. They saw little hope of getting either the King or Parliament to grant them their rights.

"We must send word to the other colonies to let them know how unfairly Boston is being treated," said Sam Adams. "Perhaps then the colonies will act together."

141

Once again Revere rode to New York and Philadelphia with the news. In twelve days, he was back with an important announcement. A Continental Congress made up of men selected from all the colonies was to meet in Philadelphia in September to plan what to do. "If England can punish Boston unjustly, she can also punish other colonies in the same way," Revere had heard wherever he went.

"Boston is as quiet as a graveyard," Revere said to his wife the morning after he returned. He could hardly believe what he had seen as he walked the streets.

Not a ship moved in the harbor, not even the ferry to Charlestown. The rope walks, the sail lofts, and the shipyards were empty of workmen. The shops were almost empty, and idle men walked the streets or sat gloomily on the wharves.

But men were drilling on every village green in Massachusetts. They were called "minutemen," for they were to be ready to fight at a minute's notice. In every town and

village, also, guns, powder, and bullets were being stored in safe places. Most of the people were certain now that some day they would have to fight England to obtain their rights.

"We'll fight, if the British try anything more," said the minutemen of Massachusetts.

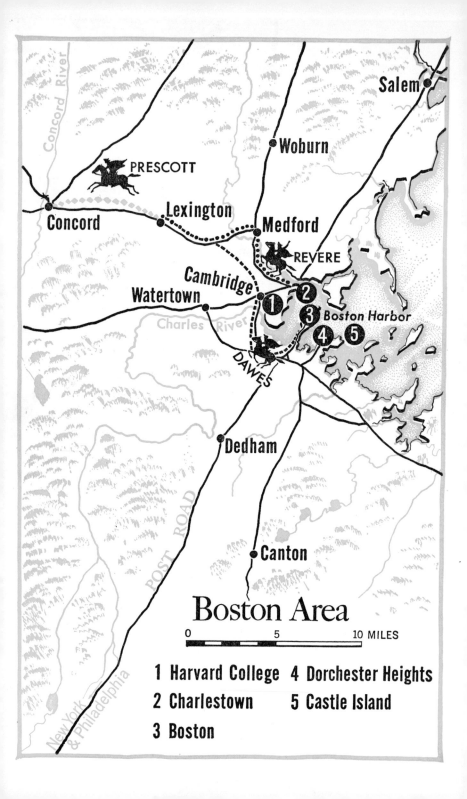

Salem

Woburn

PRESCOTT

Concord

Lexington

Medford

REVERE

Cambridge

Watertown

Charles River

① ②

③ Boston Harbor

④ ⑤

DAWES

Dedham

Canton

Boston Area

0   5   10 MILES

1 Harvard College   4 Dorchester Heights
2 Charlestown   5 Castle Island
3 Boston

Concord River

POST ROAD

New York & Philadelphia

CHAPTER 8

"Two if by Sea!"

General Gage surely knows that we are storing arms and preparing to fight," said Doctor Warren to Revere early in the spring of 1775. "We must watch the British closely, to see if they plan to stop us."

From that time on, Revere was one of thirty men, most of them tradesmen, who walked each night in pairs and watched the movements of the British and the Tories. The North End now was filled with British soldiers, living in private homes. It was easy to watch the movements of the soldiers, and overhear what they said.

"The British are up to something," Revere told his group when they met at the Green Dragon Tavern on Saturday, April 15. Others also were suspicious. They had seen boats being made ready, and soldiers preparing to march.

After the meeting, Revere went to see Doctor Warren. He was the only one of the Whig leaders still in Boston. Doctor Warren also knew what was happening. The British, he had learned, planned to arrest John Hancock and Sam Adams in Lexington because they were the most important leaders of the Whigs. From Lexington, the British would go to Concord to seize the guns and powder that had been stored.

"I think you should ride to Lexington and Concord and tell our people there what is up," Doctor Warren told Revere.

On the next day, Easter, Revere rode to Lexington. Sam Adams and John Hancock were visiting at the home of Reverend Jonas Clark.

"Gage plans to arrest you," Revere told the two men.

"When? How do you know?" they questioned.

"It must be soon," answered Revere. He

146

told them what he and others had seen and heard. "You had better plan to leave," he urged. "I may not be able to warn you again."

"We'll be ready to leave," Sam Adams promised.

From Lexington, Revere went to Concord with his news. Soon carts were removing the military supplies to a safe place, and minutemen were preparing to fight.

On the way home, Revere stopped at Charlestown to talk to William Conant, a colonel of the minutemen.

"We'll watch the British and give you a signal," Revere told Conant, "so that you can send a warning to Lexington and Concord, if I'm not able to get here."

"What kind of signal?" asked Conant.

"We'll put lanterns in the belfry of Christ Church," said Revere. "It's the highest spot in the North End. If the British are coming by land, around the Neck, there will be one light, and two if they are coming by water across the Charles."

The news leaked out that the British were to start marching to Lexington and Concord on Tuesday night. But it was not known which direction they would take. But the *Somerset,* a British man-of-war, had been moved into the Charles River. "It must be there to protect the movements of the troops," thought Revere.

A little before ten o'clock on Tuesday night, Doctor Warren sent for Revere. "The British are crossing the Charles tonight on their way to Lexington," said the doctor. "I've sent Billy Dawes to Lexington by way of the Neck. He's dressed as a farmer. You know how well he can act. If he can get past the guards at the Town Gate, he can give the warning."

Revere hurried to the home of Robert Newman. He was the young sexton of Christ Church who was to hang the lanterns in the belfry.

"The British are crossing the river to Charlestown," Revere told him. "Hang two lanterns in the belfry."

Up the narrow stairs of the belfry in the darkness, Newman climbed as quickly as he was able. Past the great bells he crept and climbed again until he reached the highest window. Then he lit the two lanterns and for a few minutes hung them in the opening. "Praise be, our men in Charlestown have seen the warning," he murmured as he blew out the lights.

In the meantime, Revere had hurried home and put on his riding boots. Two friends were waiting to row him across the Charles in a boat he had hidden on the bank.

Softly, the three men eased the boat with muffled oars across the river. The moon was just rising, and the water was still dark. Revere did not speak, but strained his eyes for movement or sound on the *Somerset*. But the British man-of-war was quiet. Then the rowboat touched land, and Revere jumped out.

There was a group of men waiting for him at Colonel Conant's house. They had seen Robert Newman's signal and had already sent messengers with the warning.

"But I'll ride to Lexington and Concord to be sure the warning is delivered," said Revere.

"I've a fine horse for you," said Conant. "It's ready."

Out in the yard, Revere examined the horse. It was small and slender, but sure-footed and tireless, he was certain. He adjusted the stirrups and the bit, stroking the horse and talking to it gently. "I'm your friend, boy," he said, as he mounted.

It was eleven o'clock. "I'll go past Charlestown Common and then through Cambridge," Revere told Conant. "That's the shortest way."

At a gallop, but not too fast, Paul Revere began to ride. He must save the horse for an extra dash, if it were needed. Just as he passed Charlestown Common and turned to the left, he saw two mounted British officers. One started toward him. Quickly Revere turned to the right. After about three hundred yards, he glanced back. His pursuer was losing ground. He would have to go around Cambridge.

Along the road sped Revere. "The British are coming!" he shouted each time he passed a house. At midnight, he was in Lexington. He rode directly to the Clark parsonage. Eight soldiers were guarding the house.

"Everyone's gone to bed," said a sergeant. "The gentlemen don't want to be disturbed by noise."

"You'll have noise enough before long," said Revere, getting down from his horse. He began to pound on the door. "The British are coming!" he called.

John Hancock looked out a window. "Come in, Revere," he called.

In a few minutes, Revere was in the house telling his story while he ate some supper. There was the clatter of another horse outside. Billy Dawes had arrived.

It was now one o'clock. "We'll go to Concord from here," said Revere. "We can give the alarm as we ride."

151

Just outside Lexington, the two riders met
Samuel Prescott, a young doctor who lived
in Concord.

"I'll ride along with you," said Prescott,
after Revere had told his mission.

About three miles outside Lexington,
Prescott and Dawes stopped at a house to
give a warning, and Revere rode ahead. Suddenly he pulled up his horse. Two mounted

British officers were waiting under a tree. In a minute, four other officers had joined them and all were riding toward Revere.

"Stop where you are!" shouted one. "If you go another step, you're a dead man."

By this time, Prescott had come up. But Dawes had managed to escape.

The six British officers forced the two colonials into a barnyard. Suddenly Prescott spurred his horse, jumped a stone wall, and was gone. At the same instant, Revere started for a nearby woods, but the officers were too quick for him. One seized his bridle. Two others pressed their pistols against his breast and ordered him to dismount.

"Where did you come from?" asked the officer who seemed to be in command and whom the rest were calling Major Mitchell.

Revere told him and the time he had left.

"And may I ask your name?" asked the Major.

"Paul Revere."

"Revere!" There were sharp outcries from all the British.

Mitchell took the reins of Revere's horse. "You'll not ride free, I assure you," he said. He gave the reins to another officer to lead the horse. "And shoot him, if he tries to run," the Major commanded.

With that, the British party rode toward Lexington.

As they came to the outskirts of Lexington, bells were ringing, and there was a volley of gunfire.

"What's that?" asked Major Mitchell.

"An alarm for the country," said Revere.

"We've no time for prisoners now!" shouted the Major. He turned to a sergeant and told him to mount Revere's horse. Two minutes later, Revere watched the British riding swiftly down the road, with the sergeant leading his own horse.

Across the rough pasture, Revere stumbled in his heavy riding boots. Then he tripped over a slab of stone sticking upright in the ground. This must be the graveyard near the parsonage. Would Hancock and Adams still be there?

CHAPTER 9

"The War
Has Begun"

The lights were still on at Reverend Clark's house, but the guests had not left. John Hancock wanted to stay to fight, but Sam Adams was against this. "The fighting here is not our business," he said. "We belong to the government."

Revere told his story. Dawes and Prescott, he was sure, had been able to get to Concord.

At last, Hancock and Adams were ready to leave in the carriage. Hancock's clerk and Revere went with them. They traveled until they came to Woburn, two miles away. Once there, Hancock remembered that he had left his trunk with valuable papers in it at Buckman's Tavern in Lexington. He decided to send his clerk for it.

"I'll go with you," said Revere to the clerk.

The bell in the church steeple was ringing steadily when the two men came back to Lexington, and there was the long, full roll of a drum. Fifty or sixty minutemen, all fully armed, were in a straggling line on the green. The sky was light gray now and the sun was rising.

Hancock's trunk was safe in an upper room of Buckman's Tavern. Before picking it up, Revere looked out a window. Coming along the road were orderly rows of marching British soldiers and mounted officers. Major Pitcairn was at the head of the line.

"Let's go now," said the clerk. The two men picked up the trunk and crossed the green.

Here the minutemen stood watching tensely, their lines a little closer now. The rows of British soldiers were coming steadily toward them. Then Revere saw the British regulars halt, and Pitcairn and two officers ride forward and shout something.

"Come on. Let's go," said the clerk impatiently.

Revere shifted his end of the trunk and moved on. Then he heard a shot. There was a great shout and a blaze of fire from the British troops. Revere turned quickly, but a big bush hid the minutemen. He could see only the British regulars.

"We've got to take this trunk to Mr. Hancock," said the clerk nervously. "We can do nothing here."

Revere stepped slowly forward. What had happened on the green? He still could not see the minutemen, for now they were hidden from him by a house at the bottom of the street.

The next day, Thursday, Revere was in Cambridge. Hundreds of minutemen had come there, and Joseph Warren was in command.

Revere went at once to Warren. "What's happened?" he asked. He had heard a dozen different accounts of the Lexington and Concord battles since he and the clerk had delivered John Hancock's trunk.

"Five of our men were killed at Lexington and ten wounded," said Warren. "But we turned the British back at Concord."

"Did you get hurt in the fighting?" Revere pointed to Warren's forehead. A lock of his blond hair was missing.

"A bullet grazed my head," said Warren.

"I was with the men who attacked the British on their way back to Boston."

Then he told what had occurred. Major Pitcairn, after being defeated at Concord, had ordered his men to march back to Lexington. By that time, minutemen had poured in from all the neighboring towns. They had fired at the British from behind rocks and trees and roof tops all the way to Charlestown.

There was great confusion in Cambridge now. Minutemen, all anxious to fight, had gathered there by the thousands. But there was little food or lodging, although Warren did the best he could to provide for the men.

"I'll serve you any way I can," Revere told him, "though I am worried about my family."

By Friday, Revere was engaged as an express rider for Massachusetts at five shillings a day. By late April, he had made arrangements to house his family in Watertown, where he was living. It was now the capital of Massachusetts.

On May 3, a wagon filled with Reveres trundled across the Neck out of Boston. Rachel had managed to get a pass, but they could not take food or anything else with them. All of them had come except young Paul, whom Revere had told to remain in Boston.

On June 16, the news came to Watertown that the colonial troops had built forts on Breed's Hill on Charlestown peninsula overlooking Boston. They had planned to put their forts on Bunker Hill, but had passed it in the night.

"I am going to join the troops," Warren told Revere. Two days before, Warren had been made a major general, but so far had no troops to command.

"You may be killed," said Revere. General Warren was one of his best friends. He didn't need to go to Bunker Hill. He didn't even have troops under him as yet. But Revere realized that Warren would take part in the battle, even if he knew that death was certain.

162

The air was hot and still the next day, June 17. "I've never known it to be so warm," said Revere to his apprentice, in the print shop where he was making paper money for Massachusetts. Throughout the morning, he had been listening for the sounds of battle.

Shortly after noon, the boom of cannon rattled the windows of his small print shop. "The war has begun," said Revere soberly. His hand slowed a little as he made the paper ready for the press. Was Joseph Warren on the hill?

Soon thick clouds of smoke were rising over Charlestown. The people of Watertown were watching from the roof tops. "The British have set fire to Charlestown" was the news. "They've crossed over from Boston under General Howe."

It was the next morning before the sound of gunfire ended. Bit by bit came the news of the Battle of Bunker Hill. The British had advanced up the hill three times. With the third advance, the Americans had been forced to give up the hill, for they were out of powder.

"How many men did the British lose?" Revere questioned with the rest of Watertown.

The British had lost eleven hundred men, one eighth of whom had been officers.

"We've taught them a lesson," said Revere. "Now they know that Americans won't run."

But the heavy losses of the British were his only reason for rejoicing. Joseph Warren had been killed. He had been shot through the head and had died at once.

The months went by. Soon after the Battle of Bunker Hill, George Washington, Commander-in-Chief of the Continental Army, made his headquarters at Cambridge.

"We have but thirty-two barrels of gunpowder," General Washington wrote to the Congress of Massachusetts in August, 1775.

The members were well aware that the colonials did not have enough gunpowder. In the past, the Americans had bought their gunpowder from England. Only a few people in America knew how to make gunpowder. After receiving Washington's letter, the Congress decided to send Revere to Philadelphia, where there was a good powder mill.

In Philadelphia, Revere went first to see Sam Adams. Adams introduced him to Robert Morris, a wealthy man who was raising money for the revolution.

"I'll give you a letter to the owner of the mill," said Morris. "I'll ask him out of public spirit to show you how to make gunpowder."

But the mill owner did not have as much "public spirit" as Robert Morris hoped. "Why should I let you Yankees take business from me?" the owner growled to Revere. "If I show you how to make gunpowder, Congress might buy from you instead of from me."

However, Robert Morris was too important for even the mill owner to ignore, so he took Revere on a quick tour of the factory.

"If only I had a plan of the mill," Revere

said later to Sam Adams, "I think I could make the powder."

"I'll see that you get the plan," said Adams with a smile.

A month after Revere returned to Watertown, a letter came to him from Sam Adams with the plan enclosed. He had found someone who had been able to get into the mill and make a drawing.

The powder mill was started in January, 1776, at Canton, Massachusetts. For the first three years of the war, it provided most of the gunpowder used in Massachusetts.

In March, General Washington occupied Dorchester Heights, to the south of Boston. The British had had a hard time during the winter. Food and fuel had been scarce, and the colonials had made it difficult for them to bring in supplies. They were helpless now, for their ships were not able to come to their aid because of the position of Washington's guns.

The British finally agreed to leave the city, on condition they could do so unharmed.

On March 17, 1776, a great fleet of ships left Boston loaded with the British army and eleven hundred Tories who were afraid to remain.

Three days later, General Washington entered Boston at the head of his troops. With the rest of the Whigs, the Reveres hurried home. "How terrible everything looks!" said the family as they toured the town.

Most of the trees, even the Liberty Tree, had been cut down for firewood. The pews in Old South had been burned and the meet-

ing house used for a riding stable. Christ Church in the North End was unharmed, but the Old North Meeting House had been destroyed.

"And the houses look like pigsties," said Rachel.

Her own house was in good shape, for young Paul had remained in Boston and shared his father's shop with a tenant.

Joseph Warren's brothers soon came to Revere. "Will you help us give Joseph's body a proper burial?" they asked.

The brothers were certain that when the British had buried Warren, they had replaced his fine waistcoat with a farmer's frock.

With the two brothers and a sexton, Revere went to Charlestown to the grave site that had been pointed out to them. The sexton dug into the shallow grave and soon found a skeleton dressed in what remained of a farmer's frock.

"But how can we be sure that this is Joseph's body?" asked his brothers.

"I can tell," said Revere. "I made two false teeth for him."

Revere examined the skull carefully. "Here are the teeth," he said, pointing to an eye tooth and the one next to it. "And you can see they are fastened with the silver wire I make in my shop."

So Joseph Warren was buried with full honors in the Old Granary.

CHAPTER 10

Bell Caster
and Coppersmith

The war at last came to an end. Cornwallis was defeated at Yorktown, and a peace treaty was signed with England in 1783. As soon as trade began with England, Revere ordered goods.

"My goldsmith trade is still my chief business," he told his wife, "but I can make money also by selling hardware."

Soon Revere and young Paul were selling everything over their counter from fish lines and spectacles to the new Sheffield plated silver which was made in England.

Times had been hard after the Reveres had come back to Boston. Not much trade had been carried on during the war. The Reveres had rented their North Square house and lived in several smaller homes. Old Mrs. Revere had died in 1777, but their home was still crowded. There were two more children now. Joshua had been born in 1774 and Joseph Warren three years later.

Not long after the war was over, Boston merchants began trading with China. They made big profits and soon were ordering pieces of silver from Revere, for he was still one of Boston's finest silversmiths.

"I need more space," Revere said to his son Paul, "if we are to have both a store and a goldsmith shop."

In 1786, Revere moved to a new store at 50 Cornhill Street* and put an advertisement in the newspaper. He would sell "pewter, brass, copper, and other wares," but his goldsmith business was "still carried on in all

* Now marked by a bronze tablet at 175 Washington Street.

its branches in the newest taste and neatest manner."

Two years later, Revere decided to try a new business. "I think I shall start my own foundry and make the hardware that I sell in my shop," he told his sons. Joseph Warren, who was eleven years old and still going to school, also worked in the shop at times. He was a much better apprentice than Paul. Perhaps because Paul's training had not been regular, he rarely made anything but silver spoons and buckles.

With Joseph Warren, Revere began to visit foundries and read books about casting in iron. Soon he had a little shop with a furnace, and was making everything in iron from stoves to anvils and hammers.

In 1792, the bell cracked in the old Cockerel Church, which the Reveres still attended. Paul Revere was one of the thirty-five men who agreed to pay for the cost of a new one.

"We must send the bell to England to have it recast," said one of the committee.

173

"I'm a foundryman," said Revere. "I'll cast the bell."

"But you've never cast a bell," said the committeeman.

"Only cow bells and house bells are made in Boston," added another.

"I'll find out how to cast a big bell," said Revere. He spoke with so much confidence that no one doubted that he could cast the bell.

Revere knew how he could learn the new craft. He went to Abington where Aaron Hobart had a foundry. Here he studied Hobart's methods, then came back to Boston with Hobart's son and a foundryman to help.

In spite of all that Revere had studied, there was much to worry about before the bell was finished. Melting the correct quantities of the different metals, making the mold, pouring the metal, and waiting the proper time for it to cool were all new methods for Paul Revere.

Finally the bell was finished. On it was

engraved, "The first bell cast in Boston 1792 P. Revere."

A crowd of neighbors and church members were in the yard of Revere's home when the bell was tested. "I'll buy back the metal if you are not satisfied," he had told the committee. Small boys pushed and wriggled to get to the front row.

"Take care, boys," he called to them. "If the hammer should hit your head, you'll ring louder than the bell."

Then the bell was sounded. The tone was shrill, but it rang loud and clear. There was a cheer from the crowd.

"It sounds tin-panny to me," said one old woman.

"It's a good strong bell," said Revere proudly. "I'll make a bell for every steeple in the country, if I'm asked."

Three years later, Revere had a new idea for work in his foundry. "I should like to furnish our ships with all the brass and copper spikes, bolts, and other gear they need," he said to Joseph Warren.

"But no one in New England knows how to melt copper properly to draw into spikes," said his son.

"I'll learn the secret," said Revere. He began to study books of chemistry then, and ask questions and observe. In time, after many trials, he learned how to melt copper and make it into all the hardware for a ship.

In 1795, the United States Government ordered six ships for its first Navy. One of the larger ones, the *Constitution,* was built in Edmund Hartt's shipyard. Revere could hear the hammering from his foundry.

"I should like to make the copper for the *Constitution,*" said Revere to Joseph Warren. "I shall write to the general government and ask for the business. I am sure I can do it as cheaply and as well as anyone."

As a result of his letter, Revere was given the contract for the fittings for the *Constitution* and also for a smaller frigate, the *Essex,* which also was being built in Boston.

"But I wish I could learn to roll sheet copper," he said to his son.

176

The Constitution *was saved from being torn down after Oliver Wendell Holmes wrote a poem about it called* "Old Ironsides." *To-day the ship can be seen at Boston Navy Yard.*

Some big ships had copper bottoms, which kept barnacles and seaweed from clinging to them and reducing their speed. But all copper for the sheathing of the bottoms of ships had so far been imported from England.

"The man who can copper our ships and free us from English control," said Revere, "can do a great deal for his country. It's a craft I must learn."

Not for a moment did Revere think he was too old to learn a new trade, although he was sixty-five years old now. He loved to do work which he did well, like making silver pieces, casting bells, or drawing copper. Shopkeeping, dentistry, and engraving he had done at times, but only because he needed money. He would have worked at the three crafts he loved, even if he lost money.

In 1800, Revere began to build a mill to roll copper into sheets. For his mill, he bought the old powder mill property at Canton, for he needed water power. The United States Government loaned him ten thousand dollars, for the Navy was anxious to have him succeed. In addition, Revere invested all his own money.

"It will take every penny I can scrape together," he told his son Joseph Warren, "but I'll take the chance."

In a year, Revere was able to write to Robert Smith, the Secretary of the Navy: "I have rolled sheet copper which the best judges say is equal to the best rolled copper to be had."

Revere's first large order was for the dome of the new State House for Boston, designed by Charles Bulfinch. His next big order was to recopper the bottom of the *Constitution* so that it could start out to fight in Algiers.

Revere was prosperous now. "It's time we bought a new house and not be renting," he told his family.

Revere sold the North Square house and bought a fine three-storied brick house with a large garden on Charter Street.

"There's plenty of room for all of us here," said Rachel.

179

All of Sara's children were married or dead now, but Rachel had six children of her own. There were also the three children of Revere's daughter Frances, who had died in 1799.

In 1804, Joseph Warren went to Europe to study bell casting and copper work. "I want our mill to make the finest copper in the United States," said his father.

The years went by. The business of the mill grew. Joseph Warren was its chief manager. His father spent more time at home and with all the civic affairs of Boston. His face still had good color and his hair was thick and white. He had a double chin now, and he was bigger in the waistline than when he was a young man. But he walked briskly and never for a moment thought that he was getting old.

He still wore knee breeches, buckled shoes, snowy-white ruffles on his shirts, and a cocked hat. "My sons can wear these new-fangled long, tight pantaloons," he said, "but not I."

However, Rachel dressed in the latest fashion from Paris. Joseph Warren proudly engaged Gilbert Stuart, the famous artist, to paint the portraits of his father and mother.

On July 1, 1813, Rachel died after a short illness and was buried in the Old Granary.

On Sunday, May 10, 1818, the bell in King's Chapel began to toll for the "passing" of someone. The King's Chapel bell, which the Reveres had made, had just been hung in the stone tower. The wealthy church members had thrown silver coins into the molten metal to make its tone pure and sweet.

One — two — three — tolled the bell. That meant an adult male was dead. Then the bell tolled eighty-three times for the number of years of the man who was dead.

"Old Mr. Revere is dead" went the word that day all over Boston. Neighbors had seen Doctor Danfurt leave the house and sadly shake his head as he told the news.

A silversmith with strong, delicate fingers fashioning a pear-shaped teapot. A bell caster listening with cocked head and pleased smile to the full, rich tone of a bell he had made. A roller of copper proudly watching a ship whose bottom he had sheathed going out to sea. A rider on a swift horse crying, "The British are coming!" as he galloped through the night.

How would he be remembered?

Author's Note

There is very little known about the early life of Paul Revere. We do know that he signed a contract to ring the bells of Christ Church, and also that his father beat him for listening to Reverend Mayhew preach. He attended the North Writing School and was apprenticed to his father, and so his boyhood was probably as it is in this story.

Most of us remember Paul Revere because of the poem about his midnight ride written by Henry Wadsworth Longfellow. Mr. Longfellow made several errors in his poem. The true facts are those that are related in this book. They are based on two accounts of his ride written by Paul Revere himself.

Paul Revere is also famous as a silversmith and coppersmith. Many of the beautiful pieces that he made are in museums all over the country, as well as in private homes. Perhaps the finest collection is in the Museum of Fine Arts in Boston. Here you will also see the portrait of Paul Revere painted by Copley and the portraits of Paul and Rachel when they were older, painted by Stuart. There is also a gold-framed miniature of Rachel painted when she was a young woman.

There is little difference in the way silver pieces are made today from the way in which they were made in the time of Revere. However, machinery is used today for molding most of the pieces, and electricity controls the heat. The decorating which is called "chasing" is still done by hand with small tools and punches. Special engraving is also done by hand. The standard of nine and one-fourth parts silver to three-fourth parts copper is still the proportion for sterling silver today.

There are many places in and around Boston to remind us of Paul Revere. The most famous is his North Square house. It has been restored and is furnished as it was in his time. It is the oldest house in Boston. Near it is the Old North Church. It was called Christ Church in Revere's boyhood, but after the Old North meeting house of his time was destroyed during the Revolution, Christ Church was called Old North.

Church services are held regularly in Old North, and the bells that Paul Revere rang are still in the belfry. The window in which Robert Newman hung the lanterns has been bricked up.

Every year on April 18, the lanterns are hung in Old North by a descendant of either Paul Revere or Robert Newman. On the following morning, a man dressed like Paul Revere repeats his famous ride. You can drive over the same route today. Every place Paul Revere passed is plainly marked.

The Town House (now called the Old State House), Faneuil Hall, and the Old South Meeting House have been restored and are now museums. The site of the Boston Massacre is shown in the paving in front of the Old State House. There are plaques to show where the "tea party" took place, and where the Liberty Tree grew. The ship *Constitution* for which Revere made copper fittings and a copper bottom is now restored and is in the Navy Yard.

If you go to Lexington, you will see the Clark-Hancock house and the green where the first minutemen were killed. In Concord, there is a reproduction of the North Bridge where the British were forced to retreat.

The great Revere Copper and Brass Company of today is descended from the copper-rolling mill at Canton that was started by Paul Revere and his son Joseph Warren. Edward H. Revere, the great-grandson of Paul, was the last member of the family with the Revere name to be a director of the company. He died in 1957.

The Reveres were also important bell casters. They probably made about four hundred bells, many of which are still in use. The largest and most famous of their bells are in King's Chapel in Boston. The first bell made for the Cockerel Church was bought by St. James's Episcopal Church in Cambridge. The church has no bell tower, so the bell is now in the nave.

REGINA Z. KELLY

We can tell the silver pieces of Paul Revere and of his father, also named Paul Revere, by their marks. The four marks on the top of this page were used by Revere, Senior. The next four were used by the more famous Paul Revere. The bottom mark was probably used by both men.

In Appreciation

There are many people who helped me to write this book. I am always grateful to the librarians of the Chicago Public Library and the Newberry Library for their aid in my research.

I also owe thanks to Mrs. Kathryn Buhler, Assistant Curator of the Boston Museum of Fine Arts; Miss Gertrude C. Doyle, Director of Educational Services for Towle Silversmiths; Mr. Richard K. Snively, Advertising Manager of the Revere Copper and Brass Company; and Mr. William De Matteo, the silversmith in Colonial Williamsburg, who allowed me to watch him make a silver bowl on Paul Revere's anvil.

I was most pleased to have Miss Anna P. Revere, a great-great-granddaughter of Paul Revere, check my book for accuracy.

PIPER BOOKS